Harnessing Land and Water Resources for Improved Food Security and Ecosystem Services in Africa

The United Nations University Institute for Natural Resources in Africa (UNU-INRA), is one of the 15 Research and Training Centres/ Programmes (RTC/Ps) that constitute the United Nation's University's (UNU) worldwide network. The Institute's mission is to empower African universities and other research institutions through capacity strengthening. UNU-INRA operates mainly from its headquarters in Accra, and Operating Units (OUs) - currently based at universities in Cameroon, Cote d'Ivoire, Namibia, Senegal and Zambia.

United Nations University Institute for Natural Resources in Africa (UNU-INRA)

Second floor, International House, Annie Jiagge Road,

University of Ghana, Legon Campus

Accra, Ghana

Private Mail Bag, Kotoka International Airport, Accra, Ghana

Email: inra@unu.edu / unuinra@gmail.com

www.inra.unu.edu

UNITED NATIONS
UNIVERSITY

UNU-INRA
Institute for Natural Resources in Africa

Harnessing Land and Water Resources for Improved Food Security and Ecosystem Services in Africa

Edited by: Effiom E. Oku
               Kwabena O. Asubonteng
               Praise Nutakor

Harnessing Land and Water Resources for Improved Food Security and Ecosystem Services in Africa

Edited by: Effiom E. Oku, Kwabena O. Asubonteng and Praise Nutakor

© United Nations University Institute for Natural Resources in Africa (UNU-INRA), 2014

ISBN: 978-9988-633-97-4

Cover Design and Layout: Praise Nutakor

Printed by: Pixedit Limited, Ghana -0203339269/ 0246409464

Disclaimer:

Table of Contents

List of Tables

List of Figures

List of Boxes

Foreword

The abundant land and water resources in the African continent are coming under immense pressure due to a combination of factors including demographic dynamics, land and environmental degradation and global climate change. These resources constitute a critical element of the continent's natural capital on which majority of the people derives their livelihoods. It is known (based on 2005 data) that the African continent's natural capital contributes up to 25 % of total per capita wealth compared to less than 2 % for the Organisation for Economic Cooperation and Development (OECD) countries. The natural resources of the continent without doubt play a critical role in the livelihoods of the people. Food systems and other key sectors are clearly associated with these resources base.

It is therefore evident that harnessing these resources for efficient and sustainable use must be of the highest priority in any attempt to facilitate better management of the continent's natural resources, in order to ensure that these resources drive economic growth. At UNU-INRA, the nexus between natural resources and economic growth is clear. That explains the importance of this thematic area to the work of the Institute.

This monograph looks at challenges facing land and water resources management in Africa and suggests possible measures that the continent can adopt to improve food security and reduce poverty. The papers in this volume originated when we, at UNU-INRA, started to reflect on entry points of the Institute's research and capacity building activities within this central thematic area of natural resources management in the continent.

The book is a compilation of research papers, written by experts from reputable universities and organisations in Africa and beyond. It aims at drawing attention to the impact of human activities on land and water resources and the need for the sustainable management of Africa's ecosystem services to improve livelihoods. Individual chapters in this book, present relevant case studies on the effects of water and land management practices including urban waste water uses, land grabbing and climate change issues. The aim is to draw lessons from best practices to mitigate their effects on food security and livelihoods. The monograph concludes with suggestions on how to manage wastelands to meet Africa's green energy needs.

The results presented in the different chapters of the book should resonate very well with a wide variety of readers ranging from university students, lecturers, researchers, development agencies and decision-makers. It is our hope that readers will find this book interesting.

Elias T. Ayuk
Director,
United Nations University Institute for Natural Resources in Africa
(UNU-INRA)
Accra, Ghana
October 2014.

Acknowledgements

This book is a knowledge product borne out of the *International Conference on Sustainable Development of Natural Resources in Africa, 2011* which marked the 25th anniversary of the United Nations University Institute for Natural Resources in Africa (UNU-INRA). The book has become a reality due to the joint efforts of several groups and we will like to express our appreciation to them for their contributions.

To Prof. Konrad Osterwalder, former Rector of United Nations University, thank you for the continued intellectual and moral support to the Institute during the pre-conference period and conference opening.

We are also grateful to all those who presented papers and especially to the contributors of conference theme one: *"Harnessing Land and Water Resources for Improved Food Security and Ecosystem Services in Africa",* which has become the focus of this book. For it is these papers, that have been included in this book after a rigorous review. It has been a wonderful experience working with you all.

We also wish to extend our sincere gratitude to the chair persons, Prof. Paul Vlek and Prof. Emmanuel Owusu-Bennoah and their respective rapporteurs, Prof. Edosa Omoregie and Dr. Mamadou Ouattara for steering the discussion under this theme.

Finally, we are grateful to all the participants who converged at the conference to share their knowledge and experiences to advance the cause of sustainable natural resources management for Africa's development.

We also thank everyone who has contributed in diverse ways in making this book a reality.

Chapter 1

Land and Water Resources for Improved Food Security and Ecosystem Services in Africa

[1]Effiom E. Oku and Kwabena O. Asubonteng

1.1 Introduction

Africa is the second largest and remains the second most populated continent. It accounts for about 15% of the world's population (World Population Statistics, 2014). The United Nations Population Fund reported Africa's population to have hit the 1 billion mark in 2010 and expected the continent to reach 1.9 million by 2050. The large population constitutes a major assert to propel the continent's development and economic agenda. However the rate of population growth in Africa does not commensurate with the available usable resources on the continent. Africa covers 6% of the world's total land area, within which it is endowed with a myriad of natural resources including land (mineral, vegetation etc.) and water. Translating the rich natural wealth of the continent into economic development for the sustenance of the well-being of its large population has been a challenge.

Over the years, the continent's populations are continuously threatened with poverty and livelihood insecurity largely due to excessive exploitation (legal and illegal) occasioned by mismanagement. Unlike the west, African economies are natural resource dependant. It is common to find agriculture and other land-based livelihood activities as the predominant sources of income, especially the rural areas which host the

---

[1] United Nations University Institute for Natural Resources in Africa (UNU-INRA)

majority of the population. These activities rely primarily on water and nutrients from land to thrive. Currently, more than 300 million hectares

of Africa's land are suitable for cultivation. According to OECD (2011), 25% of the 1965 Mha global degraded lands are found in Africa and this amounts to 16% (494 Mha) of the continent's landmass.

The annual rate of land degradation in Africa is estimated to be 1.5% per annum. Degradation of land resources and the associated loss in value of the biophysical environment hinders the provision of ecosystem goods and services that form the basis of livelihood and national development. Water, another important natural resource is unfortunately not abundant and readily accessible throughout Africa despite the huge number of livelihood and economic activities that are tied to it. The continent accounts for only 9% of the world's water resources and it is ranked the second driest continent on earth after Australia. The limited amount of water resource is not evenly distributed across the continent. It is estimated that about 51% of the continent's water resources is in central Africa alone. Aside this region, all other regions on the continent have their water availability per person below the global average of $7000m^3$ per person per year (FAO, 2010 and UNEP, 2010).

Land and water resources are critical to most livelihoods and the very existence of people as they affect food production, drinking water, health and sanitation, and production of raw materials for the manufacturing sector. Water and land resources are without doubt the lifeline to the economies of many African countries. Agriculture, and other land based resources, including water have made significant contributions to the GDP of many sub-Saharan African countries as well as the food and water needs of their populations.

Resource use demands and associated pressure from the ever growing population if left unmanaged can result in the deterioration of these natural resources. Land and water degradation are mainly driven by anthropogenic factors including poor or absence of land use plans and enforcement, resource use and management conflicts, weak institutional and governance frameworks, poor waste management system and

negative religious and cultural practices that deplete soil nutrients and
carbon and also threaten food security in Africa. These factors coupled
with climate change also contribute directly or indirectly to exposing
water bodies to siltation and high levels, and ultimately the disappearance
of some streams thereby reducing the flow of water in some rivers.

With the continuous threats posed by abrupt climatic changes and
degradation of these resources, researchers, civil society, policy makers
and other stakeholders are required to ensure sustainability. For example,
research must evolve new ways of smallholder farming in Africa that can
increase productivity to improve food security and poverty reduction but
at a lower environmental cost. Relatedly, policy frameworks must
emanate from research evidence and focus on low input low-cost green
technology for restoration and rehabilitation of the continent's natural
resources.

As urbanisation and industrialisation increase in Africa, the demand for
water and land for agriculture, settlement, industries and other related
purposes will proportionally escalate. The attendant effect on water
includes over extraction of water, establishment of urban infrastructure
in water ways and silt accumulation and chemical pollution of water
sources as well as limited availability and resultant generation of
wastewater that overwhelms management capacity of city authorities.
Waste water when not managed will find its way into the water system.
The result is poor sanitation with deterioration in fresh surface and
underground water sources through leachate pollution.

On the other hand, Africa's limited water sources continue to shrink
under climate change effects and mismanagement, widening the gap
between demand and supply of fresh water on the continent. The lacuna
has led to the use of wastewater as an alternative to fresh water which is
in limited supply particularly for urban agriculture irrigation. Therefore,
wastewater recycling and reuse is increasingly becoming an important
resource in Africa and other developing countries of the world where
water is considered a scarce resource. As more countries enter the water

stress (less than 1,700 m^3 per capita yr^{-1}) and scarcity class (less than 1, 700 m^3 per capita yr^{-1}), the production and utilisation for wastewater recycling is likely to escalate. This phenomenon has serious health implications if the right procedures are not followed and standards not maintained.

According to Corcoran, et al., 2010, wastewater is responsible for around 88% of all diarrhoeal incidents in the world, whilst 115 people die hourly from diseases linked to poor sanitation, poor hygiene and consumption of wastewater in Africa. Although, many people in Africa do not have access to adequate clean water, African cities generate a lot of wastewater (resulting from pollution by municipality dumps leachate, industrial, sewage and domestic activities). With the intensification of climate change, continuous dependent on rain-fed agriculture no longer remain sustainable option for feeding Africa and this calls for intensification of irrigated agriculture to revamp productivity. Wastewater in Africa will have to be harnessed and recovered for agriculture use and other needs. In its untreated state, wastewater is currently increasingly being used in urban and peri-urban agriculture for irrigation and it is already causing health implications.

Corcoran, et al., 2010 has also reported that well-managed wastewater will be a positive addition to the environment which in turn will lead to improved food security, health and economic gains. With agriculture consuming 70% of the water in Africa, wastewater recovery will be part of the solution. Current research must focus on cost effective green low-input technology for the recovery of "sick water" as a result of its increasing role in resolving human need for water in agriculture and other activities.

Food security in Africa, as described by the African Development Bank (AfDB), at the end of 2011 was overshadowed by a looming food and humanitarian crisis in the Sahel due to drought leaving about 12 million people to survive on humanitarian assistance. Yet, the continent is endowed with natural resources such as forests, wetlands, fresh water, fertile soils and associated biodiversity. These resources when managed in a sustainable manner hold vast opportunities for enhancing the socioeconomic status of the people and reducing poverty and hunger.

Paradoxically, African countries have continued to wallow in hunger and extreme poverty while majority of the continent's resources are wasted or remain underutilised. Of the 35 countries listed by FAO as requiring external food assistance at the close of 2011 and early 2012, 28 were in Africa. Countries with an exceptional shortfall in aggregate food production and supplies were mentioned as Burkina Faso, Chad, Gambia, Mali, Mauritania, Niger and Zimbabwe. Countries with widespread lack of access to food were Eritrea, Liberia and Sierra Leone. Countries with severe localised food insecurity were Burundi, Cameroon, Central African Republic, Congo Republic, Côte d'Ivoire, Democratic Republic of Congo, Guinea, Kenya, Lesotho, Madagascar, Malawi, Mozambique, Senegal, Somalia, South Sudan and the Sudan.

The food insecurity situation in many African countries has been attributed to many factors. For instance, Vlek (2012) summarises the factors leading to food insecurity on the continent by saying, "Africa's land is producing at less than the capacity of the land". This could be linked to the under investment in the sector across the continent. Majority of African countries' public investment in Agriculture has been grossly inadequate and constitutes less 10% of national GPD as agreed by African governments under the New Partnership for Africa's Development (NEPAD).

Similarly, UNDP (2012) has also observed that budgetary allocations for agriculture development in many African countries, is too low to make any significant change in food production. Comparatively, unmet agreed 10% is even less than the 20% that Asian governments devoted to the same sector during their green revolution period. Through the United Nations Millenium Development Goals (MDGs), the International community pledged to globally reduce poverty and hunger by half by 2015.

According to World Food Program (2010)), 26% of the globally estimated 923 million hungry people in 2010 lived in Africa. The observed relatively high rates of poverty and food insecurity in Africa is partly linked to degradation of land and water resources through water and wind erosion, desertification in the semi and arid zones, deforestation, city and industrial expansion and associated challenges of solid and liquid waste management, water scarcity and drought.

In addition, high population density, climate change intensification, lack of institutional accountability and transparency, regional and internal conflicts, high illiteracy rate, post -harvest losses, lack of adequate technologies and small farm holding amongst others have caused farmers on the continent to produce below capacity to the extent that these farmers themselves have less to eat and sell for income.

Consequently, UNU-INRA (2011) projected that most African countries will fail to meet the Millennium Development Goals (MDGs). IFPRI (2012) further reports that progress in reducing the global hunger has been tragically slow. With 2015 as the benchmark year, it is highly unlikely that African countries will reduce poverty and the number of hungry people on the continent by half, considering the fact that not much has been done since 2000 when world leaders committed themselves to achieving the MDGs. The Global Hunger Severity Index has been populated with many African countries in the "Serious" and "Alarming" categories since inception.

1.2 Chapters in the book

The United Nations University Institute for Natural Resources in Africa (UNU-INRA) as part of the focus areas of its 2011-2014 strategic plan, recognised the above enormous challenges and has therefore identified opportunities in the large human population and diverse natural resources as key factors to accelerate the socio-economic development of Africa. This plan aims at developing and strengthening the capacity for research to support natural resources management policies and decisions making among other issues. As a key thematic area of its operational modalities, the Institute therefore focuses on the sustainable use of Africa's land and water resources for improved food security. Within this context, the Institute has convened a three-day international conference on "Sustainable Development of Natural Resources in Africa", from the 5th -7th December, 2011, as part of activities marking its 25th anniversary.

The conference brought together practitioners, policy makers, researchers from across the world. Papers presented were discussed under the main theme "Creating a nexus between research and policy for sustainable management of Africa's natural resources". Participants who presented papers on the thematic area came from Ghana, Ethiopia, United States of America, South Africa, Nigeria, the Netherlands and Indonesia. Sub-theme discussions were based on harnessing Africa's land and water resources for improved food security, livelihood and other ecosystem services. This would properly address the challenges of Africa's increasing population density, climate change, poor waste management and land use intensification. As diverse as the issues were, this publication reflects participants' experiences and research on land and water resources.

Chapter 1 provides an introduction to water and land resources challenges in Sub-Sahara Africa (SSA). It provides the background and the context of the various research areas discussed by different authors in their presentations.

Chapter 2, analyses the status of Lake Bosomtwi ecosystem in Ghana, in terms of total economic and primary values using the contingent valuation method. The lake is potentially eutrophicated. The paper recommends intervention through the provision of alternative livelihood support to halt further water and land degradation.

Chapter 3 examines the changes in water, land and biodiversity of Lake Chamo in Ethiopia. Reports show that the lake has shrunk in size and declined in productivity due to climate change and anthropogenic activities within the lake's ecosystem. The paper recommends capacity development in fish pond farming and crocodile ranching to reduce pressure on the natural lake resources. It also recommends the promotion of sustainability through recycling of aquaculture waste as a protein source to improve eco-sanitation.

The impact of water management practices used in Africa was reviewed in chapter 4. The paper revealed the practices employed and potential in sequestering carbon. Scaling-up of the water management practices due to the beneficial effects on the environment is desired.

Chapter 5 reports that natural spring is predominantly used as an alternative domestic water source in the Ibadan urban area in Nigeria. Assessment of the water quality revealed that the spring water is unsafe for domestic consumption as it falls short of the World Health Organisation (WHO) benchmarks for safe domestic water. It implicated leachate from city waste dumps as the main pollutants of these springs in Ibadan and recommended adequate city sanitation as a way of improving the water quality.

Chapter 6 draws attention to the increase in volume of seawater generated as proportional to the increase in the city's population. Urban wastewater is increasingly used in irrigation for urban agriculture. This raises concerns of hygiene and the health implication of eating wastewater irrigated vegetables. Improved water governance and basic infrastructure for efficient service delivery, re-use oriented approach to sanitise wastewater for human and agricultural use were recommended.

The treatment of wastewater generated in urban Ghana is then captured in chapter 7. The chapter highlights the use of eco-technology for treatment of sickwater (wastewater) in Ghana and underscores the challenges inherent in the use of the technology identified.

The rush for the lands in Africa vis-à-vis food security and the weakness of institutions to regulate and enforce the proper contractual agreement in many African countries were examined in chapter 8. The paper found arable land per capita decline in African countries as well as an inadequate institutional framework in many of the countries.

The paper recommends the strengthening of both formal and informal institutions and the institutional framework to protect local landholding rights.

Chapter 9 discusses smallholder farmers' use of wetland for rice production and the low yield arising from farmers' reliance on traditional farming practices. Improved cultivar, inorganic fertiliser, use of herbicide and new planting techniques for the improvement of rice grain yield and supply to the local market were recommended as a new package.

Chapter 10 focuses on the impact of climate change on rice production in 20 rice producing states in Nigeria. The value of irrigated rice fields was subjected to the *Ricardian model* for evaluation of the impact of climate change on production. The study found the value of the land used to be sensitive to marginal changes in temperature and precipitation. Also, irrigation was found as an effective climate change adaptation measure. In that light, the resuscitation of irrigation system both in terms of facilities and human capacity is required for land use optimisation.

1.3 Conclusion

Papers presented captures to a large extent, sustainable management strategies for harnessing Africa's land and water resources. However, the scope of the spatial study remains limited; therefore more research is needed for the wider African context covering other aspects of natural resources management.

Chapter 11 therefore presents a synthesis of the various papers and identifies ways of managing Africa's natural resources sustainably for the benefit of all.

References

African Development Bank (AfDB). 2012. *Highlights of the food security situation in Africa. AfDB brief Africa Food Security.* Quarterly Bulletin Issue 3, July 2012.

Corcoran, E., Nellemann, C., Baker, E., Bos, R., Osborn, D., Savelli, H (eds). 2010. *Sick Water? The central role of waste water management in sustainable development.* A Rapid Response Assessment. United Nations Environment Programme, *UN-HABITAT, GRID-Arendal.*

FAO (2010). AQUASTAT Database. www.fao.rg.nr/aquastat (accessed December, 3rd, 2012)

International Food Policy Research Institute (IFPRI). 2012. *Global Hunger Index (GHI), the change of hunger, ensuring sustainable food security under land, water and energy stress.* Sourced from: www.ifori.org. (Accessed December 20, 2013).

International Fund for Agricultural Development (IFAD) *Improving access to land and tenure security.* Policy.

(UNEP) (2010). *Africa Water Atlas, Division of Early Warning and Assessment (DEWA)* United Nations Environment Programme (UNEP), Nairobi, Kenya. Available at www.earthprint.com , accessed December 3rd, 2012.

United Nations Environment Programme (UNEP)2006. *Africa' lakes. Atlas of our changing environment. UNDP, Nairobi, Kenya.*

United Nations Development Programme (UNDP) 2012. *African human development report 12: towards a food secure future.*

United Nations Environment Programme (UNEP). 2008. *The encyclopedia of earth.* Available from:

www.eoearth.org/profile/UNEP . (December 11, 2012).

United Nations University Institute for Natural Resources in Africa (UNU-INRA). 2011. *Strategic plan 2011–2014.*

Vlek, P. G. L. 2012. *Land degradation in Africa – a threat to food security in the region.* Vice Chancellor's occasional lecture, University of Ghana, December 11, 2012.

World Bank. 2008. *World bank development report 2008: agriculture for development.* Washington DC. World bank.

World Food Program. 2010. *WEP 2010 facts and figures.* World Food Program

Chapter 2

Natural Resource Conservation in Ghana: an Economic Assessment of Lake Bosomtwi

[2]*Jonathan D. Quartey*

2.1 Introduction

The sacred status accorded the remaining virgin forest lands in Ghana by local residents appears to have been the main reasons for their conservation (Nganso et al., 2012). If this argument is valid then Lake Bosomtwi, considered a sacred site by the Ashanti of Ghana should be a conserved site. Contrary to this expectation, the lake appears to be one of the most abused natural resources in Ghana. Various groups of people have expressed concern about the possible extinction of the lake if the rate of pollution continues (Otchere, 2009). Much as local protected sites like Lake Bosomtwi play a crucial role in biodiversity conservation, they are more often than not perceived by some local residents as restricting their ability to make ends meet (Wells and Brandon, 1993). Thus with growing population and its attendant environmental practices which are usually unsustainable tremendous pressure tends to be exerted on sites like the Lake Bosomtwi. Such pressures have normally been controlled by local authorities who mainly use taboos, policing and penalties to ensure compliance to sustainable practices.

However, the efficiency of the reliance on traditional enforcement has been questioned as a long-term answer to the conservation of many critical ecosystems like Lake Bosomtwi.

---

[2] Department of Economics, Kwame Nkrumah University of Science and Technology, Ghana

There is a wide recognition of the fact that the successful conservation of protected areas ultimately depends on the cooperation and support of local residents. This is due to the fact that denying the residents whose incomes are normally low, access to these sites without providing them with alternative means of livelihood would be ethically wrong and politically unfeasible (Wells and Brandon, 1993).

Local residents rely on their value judgments when they have to choose between voluntary conservation and current use of a non-renewable resource. The value an individual attaches to the resource will, to a large extent, determine whether the person will liquidate it or prolong the benefit from it through conservation.

Conservation might be better used to describe options in which the essential features of the natural habitat are maintained but some of the habitat area or some of its features are traded off for development benefits. Alternatively, the natural habitat is maintained but the resource itself is used for commercial purposes. A conserved natural re*source* might therefore be a national park in which visitors are encouraged but efforts are made to keep the natural features that attract visitors. In the same way, wildlife may be maintained for the benefit of tourists or hunters, as with wildlife areas in many African countries, wild fowl and game shooting areas in some developed countries.

Some preservationists see conservation as making too much compromise between development and preservation (Clements, 1979). In many cases, the conservation option does not really arise, since either a given habitat is preserved because it is the minimum critical natural area needed for species survival, or it is destroyed for development.

Conservation means to postpone the use of a resource to consume less today in order to consume more tomorrow. Some resources, like sunshine and permanent facilities like rivers and harbours, and perhaps labour, whose services can only to a negligible extent be either accelerated or postponed, pose no "conservation" problems, since man is not at liberty to choose between present and future use of their services.

On the other end of the scale reside the fund or stock resources like oil, and other minerals, which the earth contains in fixed amounts. With such resources it is an arithmetic truism that to use any amount at any one time is to forego the use of that amount at any other times. It is therefore clear that the choice that has to be made with respect to fund resources is the time-distribution of their use. The same is true, though it is rather more complicated, with renewable or self-generating resources such as forests (Gordon, 1958).

Eco-Economic arguments have been advanced for the conservation of natural sites like Lake Bosomtwi. The ecological argument has been that for conservation of a non-renewable resource, the rate of extraction must be optimal (El Serafy, 1989; Costanza and Daly, 1992). This is against the background that the resource will definitely get extinct one day. Thus the best approach is perceived as the optimal harvest rate, which presupposes that once the optimal harvest rate of extraction occurs, the best use would have been made of the resource.

Similarly, for renewable resources, ecological management for conservation prescribes the harvest rate which is less than the biological or natural replenishment of the resource. The ethical issues arising from wholly ecological approaches are that the use of the resource is considered for current generations benefit without regard to the welfare of future generations. This suggests a requirement for sustainable use which caters for both current and future generations' welfare. To this end, various sustainability paradigms were proposed, ranging from the very weak sustainability (VWS) paradigm to the very strong sustainability or preservation paradigm (Turner et al., 1993).

Sustainability therefore becomes a link between ecological and economic ideas for the conservation of natural resources. The weak sustainability paradigms advocate the maintenance of some critical natural capital or a constant capital stock (Hartwick, 1977 cited in Tietenberg and Lewis, 2009). The difficulty of putting up with the weak sustainability ideas stem from the possibility of uncertainties, irreversibility, loss aversion and the inability to determine the exactness of the needed critical capital stock.

This makes the recognition of critical natural capital and the constant capital rule for sustainable economic development impeded by ethical considerations. Support for intergenerational social contracts advocates the passing on of adequate capital (of all forms) as an inheritance to future generations, with special emphasis on sufficient critical natural capital stock.

2.1.1 Objective and policy relevance

The main objective of this study was to assess the extent to which the value of the lake to local residents could be harnessed for the conservation of the lake. With the wide recognition of the crucial role of local residents in natural resource conservation, the paper sought to ascertain the role the local communities around the lake could play in its conservation, based on their value system to inform policy. An understanding of this role would enable policy makers and implementers to involve local residents in conservation activities based on their interests, which normally show up in their preferences regarding the use of the resource. It will also help developers to design alternative livelihood activities that would conform to economically sustainable uses of the resource to enhance the welfare of local residents through conservation.

2.1.2 Conservation efforts in Ghana

Ghana is reputed to have well -constructed environmental policy documents. However, biodiversity management and conservation have been far from satisfactory despite the existence of well constituted institutions. The lack of coordination, collaboration and networking among the formulators and implementers of these policies has been identified as a main impediment towards progress. This state of affairs has resulted in overlaps in policy formulation and implementation, conflicts, unhealthy competitions and disharmony which drag the implementation of laudable policies to the detriment of everybody. There are also deficiencies in the capacities of these institutions, which contribute in no small way to retard performance.

Local community participation and the use of traditional knowledge in the use of natural resources as well as the conservation of nature are encouraged by government as essential towards the realisation of the goals for sustainable development in the use of natural resources. The Environmental Protection Agency (EPA) of Ghana through environmental education programmes creates awareness and mobilises public support for sound environmental practices.

Collaboration with international institutions through convention secretariats has been a trademark of Ghana as far as the sustainable development of its natural and environmental resources is concerned. It is also common to notice the full engagement of indigenous and community based governmental and non-governmental organisations working to ensure natural and environmental resource conservation in Ghana (USAID, 2005).

2.1.3 The economic justification for conservation

Despite the highly sensitive nature of conservation issues, there is the need to clearly establish an economic rationale to justify the need to conserve as against other conventional forms of development in Ghana. A general version of the economic argument for conservation is that although the demand for recreational activity and unspoiled natural areas is increasing, the supply opportunities are constantly shrinking, creating a steady rise in the implicit price or social value of natural environments (Krutilla, 1967). This irreversibility and necessary loss of future options to use these sites as unspoiled recreational or unique ecological resources create a persuasive rationale for the careful development policy.

Maintaining future options of land use for natural unspoiled areas has economic value in Ghana. This value will increase over time, due to the continued upward trend in recreation demand and also because more individuals currently enjoying the amenities of natural environment pass on the skills, attitudes, and appreciation of outdoor activities to future users and, thus, spur recreation demand even higher. The thrust of this argument is that the present population's experience with outdoor recreation results in an increase in future recreation demands.

A further economic justification for conservation in Ghana is that individuals receive satisfaction from just knowing, for example, that a 1.3

million year old lake, conserved and unspoiled, exists in Southern Ghana even though they have absolutely no current desire to float the lake themselves. This option demand, as it is called, has legitimate economic value (option value) and should be properly included as a social benefit of conservation and natural resources (Seneca and Taussig, 1979).

The natural biological environment is an ecological system of plants and animals that forms a genetic pool. From this natural genetic bank came a great variety of discoveries resulting in advances in basic scientific knowledge, development of new drugs, agricultural innovations, and other similar benefits. If this pool is diminished by the loss of a species, many future research possibilities may be foreclosed. Economic value (existence value) should be assigned to the maintenance of the entirety of the natural gene pool. In addition, the research potential of the geophysical sciences is also conditional on having available the widest possible range of natural phenomena (Seneca and Taussig, 1979).

2.1.4 Lake Bosomtwi
Lake Bosomtwi lies in a meteorite crater in the forest zone of Southern Ghana (06°30´N, 01°25´W). It is located at about 30 km Southeast of Kumasi, Ghana's second most urbanised city. The lake covers an area of about 52 km^2 (Turner et al., 1995) and has a diametre of about 11 km at its widest part with a maximum depth of about 78 m (Prakash et al., 2005). The lake is estimated to be about 1.3 million years old and yet it is considered one of the youngest and best preserved meteorite craters in the world (Grieve et al., 1995 cited in Prakash et al., 2005).

It is considered scientifically as a highly sensitive recorder of palaeo-climatic and palaeo-environmental conditions in West Africa (Shanahan et al., 2007). Plans to carry out conservation activities for the preservation of the lake as a world heritage site are being implemented, with the United Nations Educational Scientific and Cultural Organisation (UNESCO) providing the Government of Ghana US$1.5 million for the conservation project (Xinhua, 2011). Also, in 2006, a 10km wide buffer zone was established around the lake within which it is prohibited to carry out mineral exploration or mining activity (Boamah and Koeberl, 2007).

Ashanti traditional beliefs regard Lake Bosomtwi as a god (*Bosom*) born on Sunday and which provided an avenue for the departed souls of the land to converge and bid farewell to the world after their existence on earth. The story of how a wounded antelope (*otwe*) was said to have transformed itself into the lake, earned it the name Bosomtwi (Antelope god). A local festival for the celebration of its deity exists among the Ashanti people of Ghana. In times of poor fish harvests, usually considered as bad omen, the "abrodwum stone" believed to be the spiritual centre of the lake, is pacified with a slaughtered cow at a ceremony graced by his majesty, the Ashanti king (Owusu, 2009).

Lake Bosomtwi is one of the main sources of livelihood for the 24 communities in its catchment area. The communities with estimated population of 30,000 depend on the Lakes' fish stock for income and their protein needs. It is estimated that about 1200 professional fishermen depend on the Lake for their livelihood activities. (www.ghanadistricts.com/districts, Boamah and Koeberl, 2007).Apart from fishing, the lake serves many other purposes. It provides the people water for irrigation and domestic use. The Lake also serves as a means of transport and recreation for the people. Residents also derive some income from the visits of tourists to the lake even though its full tourism potential has not yet been realised. Despite the chain of useful roles the lake plays, not just among local residents but for the benefit of a wide range of international seekers of knowledge and pleasure, it faces serious pollution challenges.

The current state of Lake Bosomtwi is a major concern to many environmental minded national and international citizens. This has experienced massive overfishing over the years. Pollution has also remained a major problem threatening the existence of the lake. The use of agrochemicals around the lake, contamination from livestock, the use of detergents, the burning of organic and inorganic waste and the disposal of solid wastes in and along the shore of the lake are causing immense havoc to the lake (Boamah and Koeberl, 2007). Since these hazardous activities continue unabated, the continuous existence of services on the lake is at a great risk, since the above mentioned activities are recipes for eutrophication of the resource.

The communities along the lake are Akans and have developed a close association with it. There are several laws and taboos in place to protect the lake and fishes. For instance there is no fishing on Sundays. The traditional wood plank ("padua") is used as a boat for fishing. Also, women in their menstrual period are not to enter the water. Increasing demand for fish from the rapidly growing Lakeside communities causes a conflict between the aspirations of the local people and the aim of protecting and conserving the lake as a sustainable resource. (Dontwi *et al*, 2008).

2.1.5 Conservation and total economic value

The choice between the status quo and conservation of a unique non-renewable natural resource can be made based on the benefits (value of gain) obtained from each choice. Individuals have a number of held values which in turn result in objects being given various assigned values. The Total Economic Value (TEV) refers to an aggregate measure of all such values. These values emanate from value derived from using a resource (use value) as well as value derived from the real nature of the resource but not associated with the actual use of it (non-use value).

One crucial non-use value is Existence value (EV) which is the value that goes with the recognition of the mere existence of certain species or ecosystems. Values will be expressed through options to use a resource in the future (option value) and these are expressions of preference (willingness to pay) for the conservation of the resource against some probability of its use at a later time. TEV therefore is the sum of Use value, Option value and Existence value.

A scientific critique of economic valuation has necessitated the recognition of TEV as secondary value. The prior existence of a healthy ecosystem which is necessary before TEV can be realised and justifiably referred to as a primary value (Turner *et al.*, 1993). This makes the full value of any natural resource a combination of its primary value and secondary value.

Considering the conservation of a unique natural resource (for example, Lake Bosomtwi) where B_S, B_C, C_S, and C_C are benefiting from current use (status quo), benefits of conservation, cost from current use and cost of conservation respectively, we can write

$$B_c = TEV = OP + EXV$$
$$= E(CS) + OV + EXV$$

Where TEV is total economic value, OP is option price, EXV is existence value, E (CS) is the expected consumer surplus from use of the lake in its conserved form, and OV is the option value of conservation. Thus our rule for deciding on development becomes:

$$\{Bs - Cs - Cc\} > \{OP + EXV\}$$

Where Bs = value of benefits of current use of lake
Cs = value of cost of current use of lake
BC = value of the benefits of conserving the lake
and Cc = value of cost of conserving the lake

In terms of *measurability*, it will be clear that development benefits and development costs are likely to be the subject of well-defined monetary estimates. This raises two immediate cautions. First, since OP and EXV are difficult to measure (difficult, not impossible), there is a danger of 'misplaced concreteness'. The things that can be measured might appear to be somehow more important than those which cannot be measured. This is a false deduction for the economic values embodied in non-market preferences.

Second, because something is easy to measure it does not mean that the estimate is correct. It always pays to scrutinise the alleged development benefits. *Ex post* evaluations of development projects frequently show that development benefits were exaggerated at the time of the proposal: there is an inbuilt 'benefit optimism' on the part of planners and developers (Turner *et al.*, 1993).

2.1.6 The Model

Conservation of Lake Bosomtwi certainly implies a strict adherence to a set of rules, regulations, procedures and processes. Local residents are to a large extent aware that conservation means a loss of the resource use as the status quo permitted. Some evidence to this fact is attributing the dwindling fish stock to the various scientific exploration activities that have been permitted by the Government in the lake. Somehow, they foresee losing the lake if conservation plans are carried out. This scenario brings to the fore the need to assess the cost of conservation to the communities whose livelihoods will be affected adversely by conservation. This cost is in the form of their willingness to accept (WTA) compensation for losing the lake (based on the status quo or current usage) to the state or international community.

Willingness to pay (WTP) here means the amount of income an individual would give up to make him indifferent between the original state with income y and the natural resource at q and the revised state with income reduced to y-WTP and the natural resource increased to q* due to conservation.

Willingness to accept (WTA) is the change in income that makes an individual indifferent between the original natural resource q, with income at y + WTA and the new level of the natural resource, q*, but income at y.

It is common to find that for the same goods in the same setting, WTA exceeds WTP. Horowitz and McConnel (forthcoming) found the mean ratio of WTA to WTP to exceed 5 in a summary of 45 studies (Haab and McConnel, 2003). In very poor countries, changes in access to natural resources can induce large changes in income, and lead to substantial differences in WTA and WTP.

The determination of compensation is obtained through an expressed preference approach by the Contingent Valuation Method (CVM). The question posed to local residents was "Suppose the government wants to alter the current form of the lake so that it will spiritually be irrelevant but can still offer some services, how much compensation would you demand from the government every month to allow this to happen?"

Responses elicited here were to indicate the price at which they were willing to forfeit their control over the lake.

The spiritual twist was a way of ascertaining their maximum valuation since that has to do with higher order values among their hierarchy of needs. Generally, people who believe in a deity hold that once they please it, all their other needs will be taken care of. The aggregate WTA was thus used as an estimate of the cost to government of conservation which would also be a guide for comparison with the benefits of conservation for policy purposes.

A second value elicited was local residents' Willingness to pay (WTP) for the use of the lake as pertained currently. This was an indication of the value they currently attach to the lake. The question posed to residents was "On the other hand, if it is possible to pay to ensure that government does not tamper with the lake, how much would you be willing to pay every month to ensure that the lake is maintained for spiritual purposes?"

The progression to the decision rule then was to subtract the Total Willingness to pay (TWTP) from the Total Willingness to accept compensation (TWTA). This would indicate whether the cost of conservation exceeded the current worth of the lake to local residents, which is actually the net conservation benefit to local residents.

2.2 Methodology

2.2.1 The sample
A sample of 210 households was taken from the 24 communities living around the lake. This was done through a first stage random sample of 6 communities and then followed by a second stage systematic sampling of heads of the households in each sampled community. Trained field assistants from the Department of Economics of the Kwame Nkrumah University of Science and Technology (KNUST) were used to administer the questionnaires and elicit response from respondents. The sampled

communities were Abono, Obo, Apau, Nyinatiase, Abease and Abrodum.

2.2.2 The CVM study

The use of the CVM in this study thrived on a three-step procedure namely: designing and administering the CVM survey to elicit household values for the lake, an analysis of the WTP responses and an estimation of the benefits. These were followed by an analysis of the results obtained.

The CVM questionnaire was made up of three parts in which household heads were provided with a hypothetical description of the terms under which the lake was to be assessed. This was designed to involve government coming in to alter the current form of the lake to make it better to offer the economic services the households enjoyed, but which might diminish the spiritual significance of the lake. This provided sufficient information for respondents to consider the value of Lake Bosomtwi.

Responses on the value of the lake were elicited through open-ended questions about the lowest amount of money household heads were willing to accept and the highest amount of money they were willing to pay for conservation or development of the lake as stated in the previous section.

The CVM survey also included questions about the socioeconomic and demographic characteristics of households. These questions were on respondents' sex (G), age (A), marital status (M), the number of immediate dependents (DEP), religious affiliation (Rel), level of education (E) and household's use of the Lake (U). Specific questions were also asked about the history of the Lake (Kh) and whether the household heads believed in the divinity of the lake (Dd). The questionnaires were administered on face-to-face basis between the hours of 8:00am and 5:00pm from 22nd to 27th February, 2010.

2.2.3 Benefit estimation and analysis

The information obtained from the survey was processed by examining the frequency distribution of the WTA and WTP responses and assessing cross-tabulations between WTP, WTA and socioeconomic characteristics of respondents for validity .The frequency distributions of WTP and WTA were used to estimate the total willingness to pay (TWTP) and total willingness to accept compensation (TWTA) for conserving the Lake. The TWTP (TWTA) was computed by multiplying the frequency distribution of the sample by the total population, to get the estimated population in each WTP (WTA) interval. Then by assuming that the midpoint of each interval is the mean WTP (WTA), the population was multiplied by this mean to estimate the total willingness to pay (TWTP) or total willingness to accept compensation (TWTA).

2.3. Results and Discussion

The results of the computation of TWTA and TWTP are shown in Table 2.1 below. The results provide some crucial implications for conservation of the lake.

Table 2.1: Computation of Monthly TWTA and TWTP for conservation of Lake Bosomtwi

WTA in GH¢ (midpoint) (a)	% of sample (WTA) (b)	Total Pop. (WTA) (c)	TWTA in GH¢ (c x a)	WTP in GH¢(midpoint) €	% of Sample (WTP) (f)	Total Pop. (WTP) (g)	TWTP in GH¢ (e x g)
0	21	6300	0	0	33	9,900	0
10	20	6000	60000	0.5	18	5,400	2,700
30	10	3,000	90,000	1	11	3,300	3,300
50	20	6000	300000	1.5	0	0	0
70	7	2100	147000	2	13	3,900	7,800
90	12	3600	324000	2.5	0	0	0
110	0	0	0	3	1	300	900
130	0	0	0	3.5	0	0	0
150	1	300	45,000	4	0	0	0
170	0	0	0	4.5	0	0	0
190	3	900	171000	5	15	4,500	22,500
200	6	1800	360000	5.5	9	2,700	14,850
Total	100	30,000	1,497,000		100	30,000	52,050

WTA = willingness to accept compensation, WTP = willingness to pay, TWTP = total willingness to pay, TWTA = total willingness to accept compensation

Total Monthly Conservation Benefits = TWTA − TWTP

= GH¢1,497,000 - GH¢52,050

= US$ 935,625 − US$ 32,531.25

= Minimum Monthly Net Conservation Cost to government = GH¢1,444,950 = US$903,093.75 (Exchange rate at time of data collection was US$1.00 = GH¢1.60) Therefore, Minimum Annual Net Conservation Cost to government = GH¢17,339,400.00= US$10,837,125.00

Source: Computations from author's fieldwork (2010)

From Table 2.1 about 33 % of local residents were not willing to pay anything for the lake to be left in its current state for their use. This implied that the value they hoped to derive from the lake was negligible. This is not a strange discovery because it falls in line with the theoretical argument for common property resources. The 33 % knowing that the lake is common property are not prepared to fund its continuous use in the current state. The most substantial characteristic of (some) natural resources which lead to their excessive exploitation is that it is difficult to alienate them from common use into exclusive private property.

Table 2.2: Regression results for Willingness to accept compensation to release lake Bosomtwi

Model	Unstandardised Coefficients		Standardised Coefficients	T	Sig.
	B	Std. Error	Beta		
(Constant)	-2.9	55.925		-0.052	0.959
A	-0.943	1.071	-0.065	-0.88	0.38
DEP	-3.247	4.91	-0.047	-0.661	0.509
Rel	-141.518	94.162	-0.083	-1.503	0.134
E	-11.298	4.342	-0.157	-2.602	0.01
Ls	8.599	2.352	0.255	3.655	0
Y	0.751	0.371	0.118	2.027	0.044
U	-8.578	13.885	-0.034	-0.618	0.537
Kh	19.7	30.187	0.037	0.653	0.515
Dd	-1.502	36.887	-0.003	-0.041	0.968
WTP	23.197	2.078	0.665	11.164	0

Dependent Variable: WTA $R^2 = 0.442$ F = 15.392

Source: Author's fieldwork (2010)

No single local user of the lake can "conserve" the lake's resources since he does not own it, and what he may decide to leave for another day is can be taken by other users. Overexpansion of fishing capacity as has been done now and over-fishing inevitably follows. The most direct solution of this difficulty is unitised control, if not exclusive ownership, of the lake.

Another crucial implication of the results emanates from the modal WTA being zero. This is an indication that local residents are not willing to give up their custody of their god. With the accusation that the current state of the lake not being able to yield enough fish harvests is a result of the scientific experiments or explorations in the lake should be given consideration. Many local residents seem to believe that the solution to the current state of the lake is to get traditional sacrifices performed to restore the lake to its former productive state. The zero WTA shows how non-negotiable some local residents see the lake to be as their heritage and deity which they will not accept to dispose of.

It is worth noting that there is some demonstration of the primary value of the lake here, whose price is too high to quantify. This calls for highly skilful negotiating mechanisms if conservation plans are to be successful.

It will certainly not be easy to dispose the people of the lake in any substantial way, since by the results some are not going to accept any compensation or alternative livelihood package as payment for a transfer of the 'ownership' of the lake.

The next issue is in connection with the quantum of net conservation cost that would serve as compensation to provide alternative livelihood services for local residents. This runs into several millions of US dollars (US$10.8 million) per annum for the local residents who are willing to be compensated. This figure is minimal because there were 21 % of local residents who were not willing to accept any compensation. Here we receive notification of the amount of money going to be needed to compensate the immediate losers. This means the donation of an initial US$1.5 million by UNESCO mentioned earlier could be an underestimation if it comes to alternative livelihood activities for local residents.

To confirm that the WTA, WTP, TWTA and TWTP estimates were systematically related to the variables used by economic theory, regression analysis was performed. The results of the analysis are shown in Tables 2 and 3, with the variables defined as in the methodology.

Table 2.3: Regression results for willingness to pay to conserve Lake Bosomtwi in its current state

	Unstandardised Coefficients		Standardised Coefficients	T	Sig.
	B	Std. Error	Beta		
(Constant)	1.314	1.365		0.962	0.337
A	0.031	0.029	0.073	1.063	0.289
DEP	-0.017	0.133	-0.008	-0.126	0.9
E	0.064	0.116	0.031	0.553	0.581
Ls	-0.37	0.06	-0.382	-6.189	0
Y	-0.012	0.01	-0.065	-1.186	0.237
U	0.443	0.37	0.062	1.195	0.234
Dd	3.267	0.944	0.191	3.461	0.001
WTA	0.017	0.002	0.586	11.174	0

Dependent Variable: WTP $R^2 = 0.501$,   F= 24.601
Source: Author's fieldwork (2010)

The regression analysis indicated that the level of education (E), level of income (Y) and the length of time household heads had lived in the area

26

(Ls) were the most significant determinants of WTA. These were significant at the 5% level of significance and had the expected signs as shown in Table 2.3. The length of time household heads had lived in the area (Ls) as well as the belief in the deity of the lake (Dd) by household heads was the most significant determinants of WTP as indicated in Table 3. The correlation between WTP and WTA was high (coefficient = 0.607), positive and significant at the 1 % level.

2.4. Conclusion and Recommendation

To conserve Lake Bosomtwi, conservationists would need to inject a minimum of US$10.8 million per annum into the local economy of the communities around the lake. This would provide the needed livelihood support to keep most residents from interfering with conversation measures. Also, since about one-third (33%) of households have lost confidence in the lake as a source of livelihood, local conservation measures are not going to succeed since these community members will continue to undermine (free ride) the efforts of all others who may be interested in conservation.

The strong belief in the deity of the lake makes it unacceptable for about 21% of the local communities to hand it over to external conservationists, even though most traditional conservation methods have become ineffective. These are clear indicators that Lake Bosomtwi is on its way to eutrophication if the status quo is maintained.

The government of Ghana together with other conservation minded organisations need to intervene through the provision of alternative livelihood support packages if the eventual eutrophication of the lake has to be averted. Also, strong and careful negotiation initiatives would be needed to persuade several local residents to accept modern conservation measures to save Lake Bosomtwi.

References

Boamah, D. and Koeberl, C. 2007. The Lake Bosomtwi impact structure in Ghana: A brief environmental assessment and discussion of ecotourism potential. *Meteoritics and Planetary Science,* 42, 561 – 567.

Bosomtwi District Assembly. 2006. Accessed at www.ghanadistricts.com/Bosomtwi district on 01 November, 2011.

Clements K. A. 1979. Politics and the Park: San Francisco's Fight for Hetch Hetchy, 1908-1913. Pacific Historical Review Vol. 48 (2).

Costanza, R. and Daly, H. E. 1992.Natural Capital and Sustainable Development. . *Conservation Biology,* 6, 37-46.

Dontwi, J., Dontwi, I. K. and Buabeng, S. N. 2008. Climate Change Impacts on Fisheries Production. *In:* AGYEMANG-BONSU, W. K. (ed.) *Ghana Climate Impacts, Vulnerability and Adaptation Assessments.* 2008: Environmental Protection Agency, Ghana.

El Serafy, S. 1989. The proper calculation of Income from depletable natural resources .*In:* AHMAED, Y. J., EL SERAFY, S. and LUTZ, E. (eds.) *Environmental accounting for sustainable Development : A UNDP-World Bank Symposium.* Washington D.C.: The World Bank.

Gordon, S. 1958. Economics and the Conservation question. *Journal of Law and Economics.,* 1, 110-121.

Haab, T. C. and McConnel, K. E. 2003.*Valuing Environmental and Natural Resources: the Econometrics of non-market valuation,* Cheltenham, UK, Edward Publishing, Ltd.

Krutilla, J. V. 1967. Conservation Reconsidered. *The American Economic Review,* 57.

Nganso, T.B., Kyeremanteng, R. and Obeng-Ofori, D. 2012. Review of biodiversity in sacred groves in Ghana and implications on conservation. Current trends in Ecology ECO 34_Vol 3_1-10-1

Otchere, F. 2009. Lake Bosomtwi dying from pollution. *Ghanaian Times*, 20 March 2009.

Owusu, M. 2009. Hurray!! Lake Bosomtwi is 1.3m years old. *Daily Guide*, 21, August 2009.

Prakash, S., Wieringa, P., Ros, B., Poels, E., Boateng, F. S., Gyampoh, B. A. and Asiseh, F. 2005. Potential of Ecotourism Development in the Lake Bosomtwi Basin: A case study of Ankaase in the Amansie East District, Ghana. *In:* ALBERT-LUDWIGS (ed.) *SEFUT working paper.* Universitat Freiburg.

Seneca, J. J. and Taussig, M. K. 1979.*Environmental Economics* London, Prentice-Hall International, Inc.

Shanahan, T. M., Overpeck, J. T., Sharp, W. E., Scholz, C. A. and Arko, J. A. 2007. Simulating the response of a closed-basin lake to recent climate changes in tropical West Africa (Lake Bosomtwi, Ghana).*Wiley InterScience. Hydrological Processes* 21 1678-1691.

Tietenberg, T. H. and Lewis, L. 2009. *Environmental and Natural Resource Economics,* Boston, Pearson Education, Inc.

Turner, B. F., Gardner, L. R. and Sharp, W. E. 1995. The Hydrology of Lake Bosumtwi, a climate sensitive lake in Ghana, West Africa. *Journal of Hydrology* 183**,** 243-261.

Turner, R. K., Pearce, D. and Bateman, I. 1993. *Environmental Economics: An Elementary Introduction.,* Baltimore. , The Johns Hopkins University Press.

USAID 2005. Environmental Threats and Opportunities Assessment (ETOA) with special Focus on Biological Diversity and Tropical Forestry. Annex 1. Accra, Ghana USAID.

Wells, M. P. and Brandon, K. E. 1993.The principles and practice of buffer zones and local participation in biodiversity conservation. *AMBIO.,* 22.

Xinhua. 2011. *UNESCO devotes 1.5 million U.S dollars to help preserve Ghana's Inland natural lake.* [Online].
Available:http://english.peopledaily.com.cn/90001/90777/90855/7300 994.html [Accessed 17th October, 2011].

Chapter 3

Towards Sustainable Management of Ethiopia's Lake Chamo Biodiversity Resources: a Geo-spatial Supported Approach

[3]Alemayehu Hailemicael Mezgebe and [4]A.J. Solomon Raju

3.1 Introduction

Lakes are inland water systems with diverse ecological, economical, hydrological and aesthetic significance. Lakes of the world contain 90 percent of the liquid fresh water on the earth's surface (ILEC 2006). In Africa, the majority of lakes are concentrated along the great east African rift valley. The chains of lakes and wetlands in the rift valley support globally important biodiversity at all levels. Correspondingly, Ethiopia's rift valley is endowed with a chain of lakes with different hydrology, water chemistry, and productivity (Legesse and Ayenew 2007).

Lake Chamo is among the most diversified and productive lakes of the Main Ethiopian Rift (Admassu and Ahlgren 2000). The lake harbours diversified phytoplankton, zooplankton, fish, amphibians, reptiles, birds, and mammals. The lake-wetland ecosystem provides services for feeding, nesting, basking, and prey-catching site for its dwellers.

The lacustrine vegetation also provides hydrological and ecological functions. It plays a significant role in maintaining water quality ground water recharge, flood control, input flow regulation, nutrient cycling, erosion control, sediment traps, and microclimate stabilisation. However, the lake-wetland ecosystem is in peril because of human induced local and global effects. The threats of Chamo lake-wetland biodiversity resources are multi-faceted that would result in eco-degradation and

---

[3] Arba Minch University, Ethiopia

[4] Andhra University, India

ultimately loss of biodiversity (EPA 2005; Aregu and Demeke 2006; Bekele 2006).

From the policy aspect, it is crucial that the linkages between water, wetlands and terrestrial environment need to be taken into consideration to adequately protect the lake water resources and related ecosystems. The Ramsar Convention highlighted the holistic approach on "wise use" practices of wetlands and ecosystem approach of convention on biodiversity (Blumenfeld, *et al.*, 2009).

Pressures on lake-wetland emanate from extended cultivation, grazing and deforestation. At present, human induced effects are challenging the healthy ecological functioning of the lake-wetland ecosystem. This calls for understanding the role of wetland vegetation distribution pattern and documentation of the biodiversity resources through floristic composition analysis. The hospitality to maintain and preserve nilotic species that were supposed to be remained at the time of a connected river network of Abaya-Chamo-Chew Bahir-Turkana-Nile basin calls for strong consideration for conservation.

3.1.1 Objectives

- To analyse long-term lake level changes and its repercussions on water chemistry, productivity and overall lake-wetland ecosystem.
- To examine the floristic composition and the role of the existing wetland, riverine and terrestrial vegetation cover under natural and impacted condition.
- To identify the threats to the lake-wetland ecosystem utilisation and its conservation traditions.
- Suggest an environmentally friendly spatial oriented environmental planning for sustainable utilisation and maintenance of biodiversity resource.

3.2. Methodology

3.2.1 The study area

Location: Chamo Lake is one of the rift valley lakes wholly situated in Ethiopia. The GPS coordinates for the watershed of the lake are 37°13' 18 E to 37°40'E longitude and 05°32'N to 06°55'N latitude. Its watershed covers an area of about 2205 km² with 80 km length and 50 km wide. The lake watershed is situated at an altitude ranging from 1,105 m ASL (lake level) to 3,546 m ASL (tip of upper catchment mountain chains of Gamo) (Figure 3.1a, c).

There is a distance of 39.94 km within this range of altitude suggesting its small water-shed area to Lake surface Ratio of 7.2:1. In Lake Chamo watershed, the climate type varies from semi-arid to afro-alpine. The rainfall pattern is bi-modal, characterised by two peak rainy seasons, April - May and September - October (Figure. 1d). The Lake Chamo basin falls mainly in the inland drainage basin. River Kulfo, Sille, Sego, Wozeka, Segen, Dode and Doiso (Figure 3.1b).

Recently, there is no outflow from Lake Chamo. However, there was an outflow to Segen River through mastenfesha (Grove *et al.*, 1975). Lake Chamo is typically eutrophic. The lake also harbours hundreds of *Hippopotamus* amphibious populations and thousands of the giant crocodile, *Crocodylus niloticus*. The lake together with the associated wetland supports a variety of bird species including migratory ones.

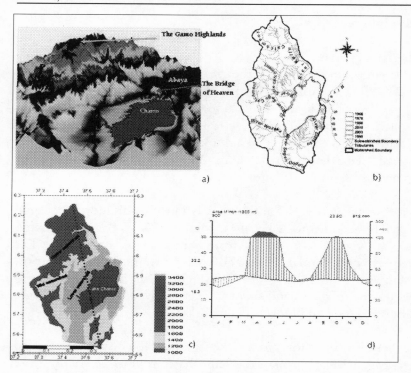

Figure 3.1: Study area a). DEM of lake Watershed b). rivers of watershed c). Relief profile and d).climate diagram.
Source: Developed by first Author

3.2.2 Methods

Aerial photographs and satellite imageries were used to assess the long-term (1965-2011) trend of Lake Chamo levels. The aerial photographs were scanned in 600 Dots per inch-adjusted scanners in tiff format. Following the digitisation, the soft copies were geo-referenced and clipped for suitable mosaicing. Finally, the image was processed using the ERDAS imagine 9.1 software for the required information. Multi-temporal satellite images of the Lake Chamo region for the period from 1972 to 2010 were obtained from National Aeronotics Space Administration (NASA) through Global Land Cover Facility (GLCF).

For consistency of information to be achieved, all same season (almost January) and cloud free satellite images were used to avoid biases associated with seasonal fluctuation in lake levels and avoid haze effect respectively. Following image processing procedures, the area of interest was digitised based on clearly visible demarcations of reconstructed shoreline positions. The area of lake surface coverage was measured using the utility measurement tool in ERDAS imagine 9.1. Following this, the data were used to examine the trend and pattern of the lake level changes. Finally, the output was compared and correlated to the overall modifications of the lake-wetland environment. Besides, causes and consequences of contemporary environmental problems contributing to the lake level changes were scrutinised.

To analyse temporal change on water chemistry, multi-temporal secondary data were collected from 1938 to 2010. A reconnaissance was made to select representative vegetation of wetland, terrestrial and riverine portions of the lake outskirt. Two pairs of transects were selected towards upstream of the watershed at the outskirt of Lake Chamo referencing the lake margin. The rivers selected for this purpose were Kulfo and Sille. Wetland and terrestrial vegetation transects were selected about 1000 m away from the aforementioned inflowing rivers. The undisturbed Kulfo riverine, wetland and terrestrial vegetation within the park area were representatives for an untouched portion of the sampling process. The lake outskirt portion outside the park territory and river Sille was taken as a representative for the disturbed or encroached zone of the lake outskirt.

In both cases, 20 metres by 20 metre quadrants were laid every 100 metre distance. Best samples of leaves, flowers, and fruits of plant species were collected. The samples were pressed on-site using a standard plant press with ample information. Finally, the samples were transported to Arba Minch University for identification and to Addis Ababa University's Herbarium for further confirmation. Voucher samples were deposited in the University's Herbarium.

3.3 Results and Discussion

3.3.1 Time series analysis of Lake Chamo level changes, causes and environmental implications

The change in lake surface coverage of Lake Chamo for the last 45 years is found to be significant. The time series analysis of available satellite and aerial photographs in the last 45 years shows that the lake shrunk by more than 14 %, which is about 50.12 km^2 of the lake surface area in 1965 (Table 3.1). The present surface area of the lake is 297.45 sq. km. The field study indicated that the lake area, earlier covered with water, has now been converted to grazing ground and used as a source of special clay with minerals which are in turn used as salt licks for cattle by Highlanders (Figure 3.3).

Table 3.1: Spatio-temporal dynamics of land use and land cover types of Lake Chamo

Date of record	Sensor	Image ID	Lake area In km^2	Perimetre in km
Jan.1965,1966 and 1967	Aerial photo	R-144 (4), R-173(3), R-206(6), R-207(1),R-255(2),	347.57	102.55
Dec. 8, 1972	MSS	LM11810561972343AAA04	338.36	102.30
Jan. 25 , 1976	MSS	LM21810561976025AAA05	339.49	102.88
Dec. 8, 1984	MSS	LM51690561984343AAA03	333.22	105.82
Jan. 28, 1986	TM	LT51690561986028XXX03	331.79	108.03
Dec. 14, 1989	TM	LM41690561989348AAA03	322.40	14.76
Jan. 21, 1995	TM	LT51690561995021XXX02	314.28	105.17
Jan. 27, 2000	ETM+ on	LE71690562000027EDC00	313.49	105.78
Feb. 4, 2003	ETM+ on	LE71690562003035SGS00	304.44	100.55
Jan. 26, 2005	ETM+ off	LE71690562005360ASN00	298.56	97.3
Jan. 6, 2008	ETM+ off	LE71690562010006ASN00	299.61	97
Jan. 30, 2010	TM	LT51690562010030MLK00	297.45	97.74

Source: Satellite images from National Aeronautics Space Administration (NASA) through Global Land Cover Facility (GLCF)

The main contributors to Lake level change include precipitation and runoff, which add water to the lake while evaporation and outflow remove water from the lake. In Ethiopian rift valley lakes, except for the inter-annual and seasonal variations of rainfall, there has been no declining trend of precipitation in the region for the year 1954 to 2004 (Ayenew 2004). The same applies to Lake Chamo.

Schuut and Thiemann (2006) reported the high variability of the average annual precipitation pattern of Lake Abaya and Chamo without showing a significant trend since 1970. Hence, a reduction in rainfall cannot be considered as a possible cause for the present size of the lake (297.45 Km^2).

Previous reports do not show the presence of overflows from Lake Chamo except the reports for the years 1917 and 1918 by Hodson (1919) and for the years 1964 to 1968 by Flacon *et al.*, (1975). Hence, overflow via "mastenfesha" could not be a possible cause of the change in Lake morphometrics.

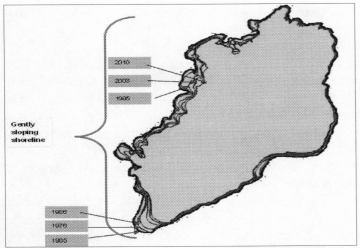

Figure 3.2: Geospatially reconstructed shorelines of Lake Chamo
Source: Developed by first Author

The other possible cause for the shrinkage could be the cessation of outflow from neighbouring Lake Abaya. Recent geomorphologic analysis of Kulfo river flood plain suggests that lack of outflow of Lake Abaya into Lake Chamo due to blocking of drainage pathway by levees possibly resulted in the shrinkage of the latter (Schuut and Thiemann 2006). The study using aerial photograph unveiled that in the past thirty years (1976-2006) the Kulfo river deposited a levee of 2 km in length across the transition of Lakes Abaya and Chamo hindering the drainage of Lake Abaya into Lake Chamo. This has been indirectly indicated by the rise in the level of Lake Abaya in contrary to the existing size of Lake Chamo.

The absence of overflow from Lake Abaya might have contributed to the shrinkage of the Lake Chamo. On the other hand, a slight increase in local temperature in particular and global climate changes in general cause escalated evaporation rates. As the rift valley region experiences moist sub-humid to semi-arid climate with evapo-transpiration exceeding rainfall (Makin *et al.* 1975), the rise in temperature and slight changes in temperature at the local level might have enhanced evapo-transpiration rates, contributing to water loss and eventually to the shrinking of Lake Chamo.

Water withdrawal from main tributaries for irrigation purposes would be taken as the main cause for the shrinkage. River Kulfo flow has been diverted and used to irrigate Arba Minch state farm (1,200 ha) (Bekele 2004; Tekelemariam 2005). Similarly, the Sille State Farms (1,300 ha) and Argoba irrigation scheme (80 ha) significantly withdraw water from Sille, Elgo and Wozeka rivers (Bekele, 2004). Further, these rivers are also a source of water for the local smallholder farms. Such practices significantly withdraw water without considering the lake's share. Hence, the downstream section of the wetland area would be in peril and may further reduce the lake size if this situation is not checked. Similar practices of diversion of water from tributaries for irrigation have been a common practice in the main Ethiopian rift valley lakes (Ayenew 2004). Therefore, it can be concluded that the shrinkage of the Lake Chamo is attributable to population pressure, agricultural expansion, poor water management. Again, the sensitivity of the shoreline towards the lake level change could also be considered as a causative factor.

The time series analysis in this study showed that the shrinkage of the lake is accompanied by an increase in ionic concentration and nutrient load. Lake level changes would contribute to change in water chemistry. The study showed that, the electrical conductivity of water has increased by over 206 % in the last seven decades. Similarly, salinity levels have also increased by 43 % in the last 65 years. The alkalinity has increased by 56 % in the last four decades.

The data also showed a general increase in chlorophyll-a concentration. The concentration of silica had declined from 38 mg/l in 1966 (Wood and Talling 1988) to less than 1mg/l in 2009 (Tilahun and Ahlgren 2009). The area subjected to shrinkage was observed in western and southern portions of the lake (Figure 3.2). These abandoned areas are currently grazing fields. The former fertilisation zones of these portions are now deserted. Algal blooming was observed at different times. The 1978 algal blooming occurrence was reported by Belay and Wood (1982). The satellite image taken on December 30, 1986 showed a huge mass of algal blooming moving in the direction of wind wave. Recently, the 2007 blooming and mass fish kill was observed in person (Figure 3.3).

Figure 3.3: Consequences of Lake Shirinkage
a. Grazing field formerly covered by lake
b. People digging clay containing minerals for cattle salt lick from pre-occupied areas
c. Algal blooming in April, 2007

Source: Photos taken by first Author

Lake Chamo harbours diversified ichthyofauna, reptiles, mammals, birds, macro-invertebrates, zooplanktons, phytoplanktons, emergent and submerged vegetations. The shrinking lake level together with agricultural inputs, cattlegrazing and exploitative fishing activity has affected the wetland-lake ecosystem. The former fertilisation zones of lakesides are now degraded and deserted. Gebremariam and Dadebo (1989) stated that the change in water level of the Lake Chamo would impact the breeding grounds of Oreochromis niloticus, a highly commercial fish species for the locals. Golubtsov and Habteselassie (2010) documented that *Labeo horie, L. niloticus* and *Mormyrus caschive* disappeared from the catches of the Lake. Dejene (2008) reported that *L. horie, Bagrus docmak* and *Labeobarbus intermedius* catches are accidental and concluded that the Lake Chamo fishery is in transition from a multispecies type of a single species dominated fishing. Lake Chamo harbours a large population of *Crocodylus niloticus* (Whitaker 2007). The estimated population of this species was 4,175 with 316 nests in the year 1992 (Thorbjamarson 1992) but, this number has been reduced to 2,130 with 262 nests in 2004 (Whitaker 2007).

Furthermore, the eggs and juveniles of this species are exposed to predators. The co-habitation of hundreds of *Hippopotamus amphibious* and a variety of birds with crocodiles is a special characteristic of the lake. Excrements from crocodiles, birds, and hippopotamus are valuable fertiliser nutrients to the aquatic ecosystem. Excess deposits of the excrements would contribute to the growth of algal blooms which in turn would lead to mass fish kills (Kilham 1982).

The present study also showed the existence of algal blooming and immense fish kills in the lake. The lake is also a source of drinking water for wild animals such as *Equus burchellii* and *Gazella granti*. The toxic nature of the lake water due to the presence of toxins secreted by cyanobacteria is causing the death of these animal species.The floristic composition analysis of the lake wetland ecosystem showed a definite pattern of the vegetation distribution; this pattern is continuous and observable. The analysis also categorises the whole vegetation distribution into belts for spatial environmental planning. The study indicated that the first 200 metre metres are dominated by herbaceous and scattered leguminous species.

In this belt, the first 100 metre metres showed the domination of herbaceous species such as *Typha domingensis, Echinochloa pyramidalis, Cynodon dactylon* and *Cyperus articulate*. The pattern of the first belt is followed by the smaller leguminous trees *Sesbania sesban* and *Aeschynomene elaphroxylon*. The cover is a stable swampy wetland with the ground fully covered with herbaceous species. Bushes and shrubs dominate the third belt which includes the next three quadrants (300 – 500 m away from the lake margin) while medium tree species showed scattered occurrence; they extend up to 1000 m in continuation of this belt.

From the result of vegetation composition study and field observations, the area can be generally categorised into three belts, namely, the herbaceous belt, the legume belt and the bush-shrub-small tree belt. These three vegetation belts have been identified in the protected Park area. However, the result showed that the encroached portions of the lake area have lost the vegetation cover as a result of farming and grazing in its catchment area. Farming practices have been witnessed near the lake shore (Figure 3.4). Grazing has not been banned everywhere except in the park areas.

Whitaker (2007) reported that the nesting and basking grounds are deserted and fragmented all along the shoreline except the lake shores in the Park area. The grazing fields of aquatic mammals have been converted into grazing and farmland. The study suggests that the vegetation cover in the Park area has to be replicated and established along the shores of the lake. There is an urgent need to maintain the observed vegetation pattern in the surroundings of the lake for sustainable utilisation of lake-wetland ecosystem. The existence of bushes, shrubs and small trees belt far away from the lake significantly slows down the wind speed or water flow towards the lake. Legumes together with other shrubs and bushes trap the incoming materials. Also, the herbaceous layer filters retain and facilitate recharge, regulation and purification.

Figure 3.4: Comparative scene of Kulfo (left) and Sille (right) riverine vegetation
Source: Photos taken by first Author

The vegetation belts collectively act as different-sized sieve screening system which slows down the pace of incoming foreign materials or sediments. Such stratified vegetation provides vital information to decide spatial oriented management interventions for the sustainability of the lake-wetland ecosystem (Figure 3.5). The first work to be taken up is to demarcate the buffer zone in the entire length of 1000 m from the lake margins. As shown in Figure 5, 41 km of the 106 km shoreline of Lake Chamo is included in the Nech Sar National Park area and hence is well protected from human activities. The remaining length of the shoreline is to be protected and restored through the buffer zone establishment with vegetation belts as mentioned above.

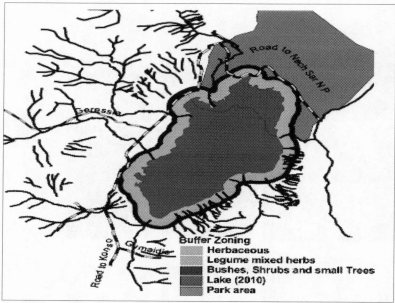

Figure 3.5: Recommended buffer
Source: Developed by first Author

3.3.2 Threats of lake-wetland ecosystem:

During this study, fish filleting were observed in six main camps out of the total fifty one fishing camps in Lake Chamo shores. Such activities generate large proportions of both solid and liquid wastes. In Lake Chamo, 1000 kg of waste (50 % of the catch weight) is discarded by the fishermen on the camps of the lake shore while filleting their catch for market (Whitaker 2007) (Figure 3.6). This significant and smelly deposition has a negative impact on the healthy functioning of the lake. It contributes to the depletion of dissolved oxygen and is a source of toxic gases such as ammonia and hydrogen sulphide. Gumisiriza *et.al.*

(2009) reported similar fish waste management problems in Lake Victoria.

Figure 3.6: Lake side waste discarding practice of fishermen
Source: Photos taken by First Author

Encroachment of grazing fields of *Hippopotamus amphibious* by pastoral and agrarian community is another threat to the aquatic resources. The nesting and basking sites of *Crocodylus niloticus* are under threat because of land use change and shoreline modification that results in habitat fragmentation. Further, poaching activities in the southern portion of the lake and disturbance by fishing activity are threats to these scarce mammals (Whitaker 2007). This calls for protection of their habitats. The other pollution problem is vehicle washing practices on Kulfo River. Washing of tanker and heavy duty trucks, tourist vehicles and other smaller cars is a common practicum along the banks of the lake. The petroleum products in the vehicles and detergents used in washing, pollute the lake with adverse consequences on its biodiversity. Such activities need to be prohibited as they are potential threats to the aquatic ecosystem.

Exploitative-fishing is also a threat on the aquatic life. According to Dejene (2008), the fishery resource is being depleted through non-sustainable fishing practices.

The study reported that the number of gears deployed for *O. niloticus* and *L. niloticus* were quite larger than recommended. He added that the average mesh size of nets used for catching different varieties of fish is below the minimum recommended size which leads to exploitative fishing. Consequently, immature stocks of *O. niloticus* and *L. niloticus* population in Lake Chamo are exposed to heavy fishing. Species composition of the catch showed that *O. niloticus, L. niloticus,* and *C. gariepinus* are important to the fishery. However, unlike catches in earlier years, *B. docmak, L. horie,* and *B. intermedius* are considered accidental in the present catch.

3.4. Conclusion and Recommendations

The defined vegetation composition pattern of the vegetation cover in the Park vicinity (protected untouched vegetation cover) calls for replication of its kind throughout the lake area. Spatially oriented environmental planning that involves a buffer zone demarcation is recommended to restore the entire lake outskirt. The lake-wetland resource could be taken as a fertile ground to establish well studied aquaculture and crocodile ranching using finger ponds for commercial fishing. Such approaches would potentially reduce the pressure on natural lake resources, reduce over-exploitation, and promote sustainable utilisation. The resource from fish processing (fillet) considered as 'waste' could be used as a cheap source of protein for livestock feeds. This is a win-win principle for eco-sanitation.

References

Admassu, D. and Ahlgren, I. 2000. Growth of juvenile tilapia, Oreochromis niloticus L. from Lakes Zwai, Langeno and Chamo (Ethiopian rift valley) based on otolith micro increment analysis. *Ecological Freshwater Fish,* 9, 127-137.

Aregu, L. and Demeke, F. 2006. Socio-economic survey of Arba-Minch riverine forest and woodland.*Journal of Drylands,* 1 194-205.

Ayenew, T. 2004. Recent changes in the level of Lake Abiyata, Central Main Ethiopian Rift. *Hydrological Science Journal,* 47, 493-503.

Bekele, S. 2004. Assessment of irrigation potential and investigation of impact on the Abaya-chamo lakes.*IWMI Conference Papers.* Addis Ababa, Ethiopia.

Bekele, S. 2006. Modelling natural conditions and impacts of consumptive water use and sedimentation of Lake Abaya and Lake Chamo, Ethiopia.*Lakes and Reservoirs: Resources. and Management,* 11 73-82.

Belay, A. and Wood, R. B. 1982. Limnological aspects of an algal bloom on Lake Chamo in Gamo Goffa Administrative Region of Ethiopia.*Ethiopia Journal Science,* 5 1-19.

Blumenfeld, S., Lu, C., Christophersen, T. and Coates, D. 2009. Water, Wetlands and Forests: of Ecological, Economic and Policy Linkages. *CBD Technical Series No 47.*

Dejene, Z. 2008. *Impact of fisheries and water quality changes on the management of Lake Chamo.*MSc, Addis Ababa University.

Environmental Protection Authority (EPA) 2005.Management plan for the conservation and sustainable utilisation of Abaya and Chamo wetland.Addis Ababa Ethiopia.

Falcon, N. L., Grove, A. T., Schove, D. J., Banister, K. E., Kingham, T. J., King, R. B., Lamb, H. H., Kent, P. and Peters, E. R. 1975. Lake Levels and climatic change in the rift valley of southern Ethiopia: Discussion. . *The Geogr. J,* 141, 194-202.

Gebremariam, Z. and Dadebo, E. 1989.Water resources and fisheries management in the rift valley lakes.*SINET Ethiop J Sci,* 12 95-109.

Golubtsov, A. S. and Habteselassie, R. 2010. Fish faunas of the Chamo-Abaya and Chew Bahir basins in southern portion of the Ethiopian Rift Valley: origin and prospects for survival. *Aquatic Ecosystem Health & Management* 13, 47-55.

Grove, A. T., Street, F. A. and Goudie, A. S. 1975.Former lake levels and climatic change in the Rift Valley of southern Ethiopia.*Geogr J,* 141 177-202.

Gumisiriza, R., Mshandete, A., Thomas, M., Rubindamayugi, T., Kansiime, F. and Kivaisi, A. 2009. Nile perch fish processing waste along Lake Victoria in East Africa: Auditing and characterisation. *African J. Env. Sci. and Tech,* 3, 13-20.

Hodson, A. W. 1919. Southern Abyssinia.*Geogr J,* 53, 65-83.

International Lake Environment Committee (ILEC) 2006.Towards the promotion of integrated lake basin management.*International Lake Environment Committee Newsletter,* 48, 4-5.

Kilham, P. 1982. The Effect of Hippopotamuses on potassium and phosphate ion concentrations in an African lake. *Am Midland Nat,* 108, 202-205.

Legesse, D. and Ayenew, T. 2007. The changing face of the Ethiopian rift lakes and their environs: call of the time. *Lakes Reservoirs Research and Management,* 12, 149-165.

Makin, M. J., Kingham, T. J., Waddams, A. E., Birchall, C. J. and Teferra, T. 1975. Development prospects in the southern rift valley, Ethiopia. . *Land Resources Studies* Ethiopia: Land Resources Division, Ministry of Overseas Development.

Schutt, B. and Thiemann, S. 2006. Kulfo river, south Ethiopia as a regulator of lake level changes in lake Abaya- Chamo system. *Zbl. Geol. Palaont. Teil,* 1, 129-143.

Teklemariam, A. 2005.*Water quality monitoring in Lake Abaya and Lake Chamo Region.*PhD, University of Siegen Germany.

Thorbjrnarson, J. 1992. Crocodiles: an action plan for their conservation. . Gland, Switzerland: IUCN.

Tilahun, G. and Ahlgren, G. 2009. Seasonal variations in phytoplankton biomass and primary production in the Ethiopian Rift Valley lakes Ziway, Awassa and Chamo-The basis for fish production.*Limnologica,* 40 SRC - GoogleScholar, 330-342.

Whitaker, R. 2007. Sustainable use of the Lake Chamo Nile Crocodile Population Project Document.Ethiopia.: African Parks.

Wood, R. B. and Talling, J. F. 1988.Chemical and algal relationships in a salinity series of Ethiopian inland waters.*Hydrobiolo gia* 158, 29-67.

Chapter 4

Review of Carbon Sequestration under some Agricultural Water Management Practices

[5]Oladimeji Oladele and [6]Ademola Braimoh

4.1   Introduction

The vast majority of the population in Sub-Saharan Africa (SSA) make their living from rain-fed agriculture. Many of them depend to a large extent on smallholder subsistence agriculture for their livelihood security. Yet an estimated 38 % of the population (roughly 260 million people) live in drought-prone dry lands (UNDP/UNSO, 1997). Rain-fed agriculture is most significant in SSA where it accounts for about 96% of the cropland. As a result, economic development in SSA remains particularly vulnerable to the vagaries of rainfall, which can be aggravated by the effect of climate change.

Falkernmark(1986) maintained that there is a correlation between poverty, hunger and water stress. Recurrent droughts and dry spells lead to food shortages and famine and continuous degradation of natural resources. This in turn reduces resilience and increases vulnerability to the next dry spell, in a vicious circle. Water scarcity is a significant problem for farmers in Africa, where 80–90% of water withdrawals are used for agriculture (FAO/IIASA, 2000; Rosegrant et al., 2002). The single most limiting factor for crop growth in the dry lands is water availability in the crop root zone for biomass production (Falkenmark & Rockstrom, 1993;Falkenmark and Rockstrom 2004; Lal, 1991) and this

[5] Department of Agricultural Economics and Extension, North-West University, South Africa

[6] Agricultural and Rural Development, The World Bank, USA

limiting factor explains the large gap between actual and potential yields in dry land farming systems (Rijks, 1986) where recurrent water scarcity erodes yield potential.

Yields can be significantly enhanced by improved water management, particularly by increasing water availability and the water uptake capacity of crops. According to Lal (1997), a key condition to increase soil productivity in SSA is to ensure an effective water infiltration and storage in the soil. The soil's water-holding capacity is intimately linked to its texture, structure and organic matter content (Hillel, 1980).

One of the major Millennium Development Goals (MDGs) is to reduce poverty and hunger. Integrated land and water management could play a key role in achieving this goal, especially in increasing food production. Appropriate technologies have been developed and are effective for increasing crop production in dry areas, but in view of severe land degradation in the dry land zones of Africa, integrated rainwater harvesting and soil water conservation (RWH/SWC) can also further enhance the effectiveness of these technologies.

They can also be used to rehabilitate degraded land, retain moisture, and re-establish vegetation cover to improve crop production in order to alleviate poverty and enhance food security. Two major factors characterising agriculture in the dry lands are: (i) erratic climatic conditions with frequent periods of water shortages (Sivakumar and Wallace 1991; Stroosnijder and Van Rheenen 2001), and (ii) the presence of large areas of inherently low fertility and crust prone soils (Morin 1993; Breman et al., 2001).

The adoption by farmers of agricultural practices that ensure efficient rainfall utilisation for dry land production of a wide variety of crops is essential for the production, economic and social sustainability. Water harvesting is one option that increases the amount of water per unit cropping area which in turn reduces drought impact. In Burkina Faso and Niger, farmers have developed soil and water conservation techniques such as water harvesting, slope and barriers to reduce soil erosion and land degradation. Most of these methods are multifunctional and consist of rainwater harvesting and soil water conservation technologies which at the same time maintain the soil organic matter status as well as the physical properties of the soil.

Rainwater harvesting (RWH) is the method of inducing, collecting, storing and conserving local surface runoff for agricultural production. In Africa, the different RWH techniques were introduced long back and are still in use today. Countries like Zimbabwe, Kenya, Swaziland and Ethiopia have since introduced some of the techniques of RWH such as *fanya juu*, infiltration pits and tied ridges in communal areas (Reij et al., 1996).

According to Bainbridge (1998), the infiltration pits improve water infiltration rate, water retention, reduces evaporation, increase surface storage and the time available for infiltration to occur. Stern et al. (1992) at Roodeplaant showed that Putin was beneficial in reducing surface runoff, maintained higher plant evapo-transpiration rates and yields. In Burkina Faso, the *"zaï"* is a traditional technique for enhancing soil moisture through the use of stone strips, which are arranged perpendicular to the slope of the land in order to slow down water flow, encourage water infiltration and increase the sedimentation of the materials reconstituting soil (Sidibe 2005).

In Ethiopia, several indigenous technologies developed to control soil erosion and conserve soil water include cut-off drains locally called *"Boraatii* and drainage furrow called *'Bo'oo' or 'yaa'a"*. Depending on the runoff expected, which depends on the slope length and gradient, the intensity of rainfall and the type of crop planted upstream on the field: re-enforcement may be necessary (Erkossa and Ayele 2003).

Farmers are not primarily concerned about water-use efficiency (WUE), but ensuring a stable soil moisture and consequently, stable crop yield over time remains a concern. RWH systems do not necessarily focus on improving WUE, but primarily to reduce the huge variability in potential and actual yield gaps over time. Major endeavour for dry land farmers is to maximise the infiltration of rainfall to the root zone, and avoid periods of water stress during the cultivation seasons. At the same time, soil issues, especially soil fertility, water-holding capacity and soil surface conditions, are intimately linked to watering issues, in determining the potential for biomass production (Fox and Rockstrom 2000).

Rainwater Harvesting (RWH) refers to all technologies where rainwater is collected to make it available for agricultural production, domestic purposes or industrial use. RWH aims to minimise the effects of seasonal variations in water availability due to droughts and dry periods and to enhance the reliability of agricultural production. A RWH system usually consists of three components: (1) a catchment / collection area which produces runoff because the surface is impermeable or infiltration is low; (2) a conveyance system through which the runoff is directed e.g. by bunds, ditches, channels (though not always necessary); (3) a storage system (target area) where water is accumulated or held for use - in the soil, in pits, ponds, tanks or dams. When water is stored in the soil - and used for plant production there - RWH often need additional measures to increase infiltration in this zone, and to reduce evaporation loss, for example by mulching.

Furthermore soil fertility needs to be improved by composting /manuring, or micro-dosing with inorganic fertilisers. A Smallholder Irrigation Management (SIM) unit is typically a plot covering an area less than 0.5 ha. SIM schemes may be managed either by an individual land user or by groups / communities. The guiding principle of sustainable SIM is 'more crops per drop', in other words efficiency of water use. This can be achieved through more efficient (1) water collection and abstraction; (2) water storage; (3) distribution and; (4) water application in the field. Two main categories of SIM can be distinguished, traditional surface irrigation systems and recent micro-irrigation systems including drip irrigation. Micro-irrigation systems, are commonly used for, and are very important in the production of vegetables, fruits and flowers.

Cross-slope barriers are measured on sloping lands in the form of earth or soil bunds, stone lines, and/or vegetative strips for reducing run-off velocity and soil loss, thereby contributing to soil, water and nutrient conservation. This is achieved by reducing steepness and/or length of slope (Mulugeta and Stahr, 2010). Terraces are not usually constructed per se, but rather develop gradually behind earth bunds, vegetative strips (usually grass) or stone barriers, due to soil movement from the upper to the lower part of the terrace.

The adoption of water management practices has several implications for climate change. The primary goal of water management practices is the enhancement of soil moisture, which consequently affects the soil carbon. Prominent among the mitigation and adaptation strategies is the improvement and increasing of soil carbon stocks (Ringler, et al 2010). Water harvesting for crop production, if successfully implemented within a social and hydrological catchment, will have many interacting implications on biophysical, economic, and ecological systems, suggesting that a systems approach is advisable when developing water management approaches. The objective of this paper is to examine water management practices used in Africa such as rain water harvesting, slope/barriers and terracing and the impact of such practices on carbon sequestration and climate-change mitigation.

4.2. Materials and Methods

The method used in this paper recognised the constraints stated by Vagen *et al.*, (2005) that there are important limits and constraints to current estimates of Soil organic carbon (SOC) stocks in SSA, as it relates to uncertain in estimates of, soil bulk density due to methodological problems. The methods used by different authors are different which contributes to the uncertainty in estimates. Further, results from different studies are reported for different depths (e.g., 0–10, 0–20, 0–30 cms), which complicates the assessment of changes in SOC stocks and necessitates an adjustment to enable comparisons of different studies.

In this study, a review of the scientific literature on soil carbon sequestration in Africa was carried out to assess the greenhouse-gas mitigation potential of different water management practices such as rain water harvesting, slope/barriers and terracing using on-line scholarly and scientific databases. The review covered carbon sequestration field measurements and estimates derived from models. All the studies reviewed adopted formal experimental designs, setting up control and treatments. The variations applied in the treatments accounted for the different levels of carbon added to the soil. Most studies reported concentrations of carbon in soil samples (C_c in g kg^{-1}). These were converted to volumes and then areas to calculate stocks (C_s in kg $^{-1}$ ha^{-1}) and sequestration rates (kg ha^{-1} yr^{-1}) using bulk density (BD in g cm^{-3}) and sample soil depth (D, in cm):

$$C_s = BD \times C_c \times D \times 10000 \qquad (1)$$

In a few studies, the values were given in terms of % soil organic matter. In these cases concentrations of C_c (g kg^{-1}) were calculated as follows (Guo and Gifford, 2002):

$$C_c = 0.58 \times OM\% \times 10 \qquad (2)$$

In some cases only a single value, either initial or average across treatments, was provided for bulk density. In these cases, value was assumed to apply to all treatments. No corrections were made for changes in bulk density among treatments (for instance to be soil-equivalent mass), but if the authors made these adjustments, they were used. The effect of a practice was normally estimated by comparing the final level of soil carbon stock in one treatment with that practice and an appropriate control.

Thus, soil carbon sequestration rate estimates in this paper are estimates of effect size – the difference with respect to a control – and thus represent the additional or marginal benefit of practice change. The analyses carried out in this report were kept simple, given constraints in the dataset. Effect sizes and importance of contextual variables was summarised by means and 95% confidence intervals for the mean.

The amount of carbon sequestered by each water management practice covered in this study was translated into climate-change mitigation benefits. To convert C to CO_2, the mean carbon sequestered was multiplied by 3.57 and then expressed per thousand (IPCC, 2007).

$$(C_{sequestered} \times 3.57)/1000$$

4.3. Results and Discussion

4.3.1 Rates of soil carbon sequestration by water management practices

In Table 4.1, the average carbon sequestered under rain water harvesting from 33 estimates was 839 kg C ha^{-1} yr^{-1}. This practice is particularly important to farmers in the semi-arid and arid region where there are a few days of rains but rain-fed agriculture is practiced. The practices of cross slope barriers (22 estimates) and terracing (15 estimates) sequester additional carbon at the mean rate of 1193 and 421 kg C ha^{-1} yr^{-1} respectively. This is very critical in regions of high undulating surfaces and the highlands (Tematio *et al.*, 2004). Barry et al (2008) reported that commonly used RWH techniques can be divided into micro-catchments collecting water within the field and macro-catchments collecting water from a larger catchment further away with potential for C sequestration (tonnes/ha/year) being 0.26-0.46. Liniger et al (2011) identified traditional surface irrigation systems and recent micro-irrigation systems including drip irrigation and stated that their potential for C sequestration (tonnes/ha/year) is 0.15. Zougmore *et al.,* (2002) noted that erosion between the barriers helps to achieve the levelling of the terrace bed and its potential for carbon sequestration is 0.5-1.0tonnes/ha/year.

Table 4.1: Observed rates of soil carbon sequestration under different water management practices

Carbon sequestration kg C ha^{-1}yr^{-1}

Water management	Mean	Lower 95% CI of mean	Upper 95% CI of mean	Min	Max	Number of estimates
Water harvesting	839	556	1122	103	3170	33
Slope/barriers	1193	581	1805	151	4615	22
Terracing	421	276	566	60	990	15

Source: Compiled by the authors

4.3.2 Greenhouse gas mitigation potential of the studied water management practices

From Table 4.2, the amount of carbon sequestered by each water management practice covered in this study was translated into climate-change mitigation benefits. The carbon sequestered was calculated in terms of $tCO_2eha^{-1} yr^{-1}$. Table 4.2 presents the different values for each water management practice based on the mean amount of carbon sequestered. The use of slope / barriers and water harvesting have the highest climate change mitigation potential 5.27 and 3.97t $CO_2 eha^{-1} yr^{-1}$ respectively. Land emissions are the differences among conventional and improved practices for nitrous oxides and methane expressed in CO_2 equivalents. The net impact is the sum of the three columns. Process emissions are those arising from fuel and energy-use. It then implies that the higher the amount of soil carbon sequestered by a water management practice, the lower the land and process emissions, the higher the climate change mitigation potential.

These practices will among other considerations for other factors be interpreted cautiously as being effective for climate change mitigation. Major issues arising from these findings are that sequestration of carbon in the soil through changes in water management practices may be more difficult than experiments studies have shown. Also, the ability of a water management practice to achieve additional soil carbon does not automatically imply a net decrease in greenhouse-gas emissions.

Table 4.2: Climate Change mitigation benefits of land management practices

Land management practices	Mitigation potential $tCO_2eha^{-1} yr^{-1}$	Land Emissions[a] N_2O and CH_4 $t CO_2e ha^{-1} yr^{-1}$	Process Emissions[a] $t CO_2e ha^{-1} yr^{-1}$	Net Impact $t CO_2e ha^{-1} yr^{-1}$
Water harvesting	3.08	0.66	0.23	3.97
Slope/barriers	4.38	0.66	0.23	5.27
Terracing	1.55	0.66	0.23	2.44

Source: Compiled by the authors

4.4 Conclusion

This review has revealed that there is a high potential to sequester additional carbon through water management practices. The most prominent water management practice is the use of the slope and barriers. The performance of these water management practices depends on soil properties and climatic conditions, and the degree of soil degradation at the time of intervention. The potential of these water-management practices for climate change mitigation as found in the review should not be selectively considered but explored in the context of factors that may affect the application of each land-management practice and the prevailing conditions. There is a need to integrate these water management practices for carbon sequestration into larger sustainable development and livelihood's strategies and practices in order to enhance a holistic approach and reduce some of the constraints that may inhibit these positive effects of land management practices for carbon sequestration.

References

Bainbridge, D. A. 1998. *A handbook for erosion control and watershed rehabilitation, Hungry Valley.,* San Diego, CA, SERG/USIS ESP for State Parks OHMVRA.

Barry, B., Olaleye, A. O., Zougmoré, R. and Fatondji, D. 2008. Rainwater harvesting technologies in the Sahelian zone of West Africa and the potential for out scaling. Colombo, Sri Lanka. International Water Management Institute.

Breman, H., Groot, J. J. R. and van Keulen, H. 2001. Resource limitations in Sahelian agriculture. *Global Environmental Changes,* 11, 59-68.

Erkossa T and Gezahegn Ayele. 2003. Indigenous Knowledge and Practices for Soil
and Water Management in East Wollega, Ethiopia. In:C.Wollny, A. Deininger, N. Bhandari, B.Maass, W.Manig, U.Muuss, F.Brodbeck, I.Howe (eds) Technological and Institutional Innovations for Sustainable Rural Development. Deutscher Tropentag 2003. www.tropentag.de.

Falkenmark, M. 1986 Fresh water-time for a modified approach.*Ambio* 15, 192-200.

Falkenmark, M. and Rockstrom, J. 1993. Curbing rural exodus from tropical dry lands.*Ambio,* 12, 2-7.

Falkenmark, M. and Rockström, J. 2004. *Balancing Water for Humans and Nature: the New Approach in Ecohydrology,* London, U. K., Earth scan.

FAO/IIASA 2000. Global agroecological zones (Global-AEZ) CD-Rom. http://www.iiasa.ac.at/Research/LUC/GAEZ

Fox, P. and Rockstrom, J. 2000. Water harvesting for supplementary irrigation of cereal crops to overcome intra-seasonal dry spells in the Sahel. *Phys. Chem. Earth,* 25, 289-296.

Guo, L. and Gifford, R. 2002. Soil carbon stocks and land use change: a meta analysis. *Global Change Biology,* 8, 345-360.

Hillel, D. 1980. *Applications of Soil Physics,* New York, Academic Press New.

Lal, R. Current research on crop water balance and implications for the future .*In:* SIVAKUMAR, M. V. K., WALLACE, J. S., RENARD, C. and GIROUX, C., eds. International Workshop 1991 Niger. IAHS publication

Lal, R. 1997. Soil quality and sustainability. *In:* BLUM, W. H., VALENTIN, C. and STEWART, B. A. (eds.) *Methods for Assessment of Soil Degradation.* Boca Raton: CRC Press.

Liniger, H. P., Mekdaschi Studer, R., Hauert, C. and Gurtner, M. 2011. SustainableLand Management in Practice – Guidelines and Best Practices for Sub-Saharan Africa. World Overview of Conservation Approaches and Technologies (WOCAT) and Food and Agriculture Organisation of the United Nations (FAO).

Morin, J. 1993. Soil crusting and sealing in West Africa and possible approaches to improved management. *Soil tillage in Africa needs and challenges*

Mulugeta, D. and Karl, S. 2010. Assessment of integrated soil and water conservation measures on key soil properties in South of Gonder, North-Western Highlands of Ethiopia. *Journal of Soil Science and Environmental Management,* 17, 164-176.

Reij, C., Scoones, I. and Toulmin, C. 1996. *Sustaining the Soil: Indigenous soil and water conservation in Africa,* London, Earthscan.

Rijks, D. Development of rainfed agriculture under arid and semiarid conditions.The environment - assessing the problems. *In:* DAVIS, T. J., ed. Sixth agricultural sector symposium, 1986 Washington, D. C.: World Bank, 133-152.

Ringler, C., Zhu, X., Cai, J., Koo, D. and Wang, T. 2010. Climate Change Impacts on Food Security in Sub-Saharan Africa: Insights from Comprehensive Climate Change Scenarios. *IFPRI Discussion Paper* Washington, DC, USA International Food Policy Research Institute.

Rosegrant, M., Ximing, C., Cline, S. and Nakagawa, N. 2002. The Role of Rainfed Agriculture in the Future of Global Food Production. *EPTD Discussion Paper* Washington, DC, USA International Food Policy Research Institute (IFPRI).

Sidibé, A. 2005.Farm-level adoption of soil and water conservation techniques in northern Burkina Faso *Agricultural Water Management* 71, 211-224.

Sivakumar, M. V. K., Wallace, J. S., Renard, C. and Giroux, C. Soil water balance in the Sudano-Sahelian zone: need, relevance and objectives of the workshop. *In:* SIVAKUMAR, M. V. K., WALLACE, J. S., RENARD, C. and GIROUX, C., eds. International Workshop on Soil Water Balance in the Sudano-Sahelian Zone, , 1991 Niamey. Wallingford, UK: Institute of Hydrology, 3-10.

Stern, R., Vander Marwe, A. J., Laker, M. C. and Shainberg, I. 1992. Effects of soil surface treatment on runoff and wheat yield under irrigation. ". *Agron. J.,* 84, 114-119.

Stroosnijder, L. and Van Rheenen, T. 2001. Agro-sylvo-pastoral land use in Sahelian villages.*Advance in Geoecology,* 33 408.

Tematio, P. L., Kengni, D., Bitom, M., Hodson, J. C., Fopoussi, O., Leumbe, H. G., Mpakam, D. and Tsozué 2004. Soils and their distribution on Bambouto volcanic mountain, West Cameroon highland, Central Africa. *Journal of African Earth Sciences,* 39, 447-457.

UNDP/UNSO 1997. Aridity zones and dry land populations: an assessment of population levels in the world's dry lands with particular reference to Africa. . New York: UNDP Office to Combat Desertification and Drought (UNSO).

Vangen, T. G., Lal, R. and Singh, B. R. 2005. Soil carbon sequestration in sub-Saharan Africa: A review. . *Land Degradation & Development,* 16, 53-71.

Zougmore, R., Gnankambary, Z., Guillobez, S. and Stroosnijder, L. O. 2002. Effect of stone lines on soil chemical characteristics under continuous sorghum cropping in semiarid Burkina Faso". . *Soil & Tillage Research,* 66**,** 47-53.

Chapter 5

An Assessment of the Quality of Natural Spring Water Used as Alternative Domestic Water Sources in Ibadan, Nigeria

[7]Grace Adeniji-Oloukoi and [8]Tunde Agbola

5.1   Introduction

The challenge of water supply shortages is not just the issue of quantity available per capita per day. The health-related concerns make it necessary to consider the quality of the available water supply sources to urban dwellers. Noting with interest that water-related diseases such as cholera and diarrhoea, which claimed the lives of 2.5 million people in 2008, among which 1.3 million were children under the age of five (WHO, 2011).

The current standard by the WHO and UNICEF (2003) described reasonable access to an improved water supply as the availability of at least 20 litres per person per day from a source not more than one kilometre from the dwelling. But, whenever and wherever there is an inadequacy (qualitatively and quantitatively), supplies of uncontaminated water are very critical (Prüss-Üstün, et al. 2008).

Water quality may be more important than quantity for maintaining human health (Zhao et al. 1997; WHO, 2000). This is because the human right to water entitles everyone to sufficient, affordable, accessible, safe and acceptable water for personal and domestic uses (UNESCO, 2002). Safety and acceptability are the key indicators of

---

[7]Department of Environmental Management, Lead City University, Nigeria

[8] Department of Urban and Regional Planning, University of Ibadan, Nigeria

water quality which are so important that a special rapporteur, Ms. Catarina de Albuquerque, on the human right to safe drinking water and sanitation was appointed in September 2008 to examine these crucial issues and provide recommendations to Governments, the United Nations and other stakeholders for policy considerations (UN, 2009)

Ashbolt et al. (2001), provide a model to explain the interconnectivity between public health status and the quality of water for drinking purposes. The model indicates that periodic assessment of quality of water supply sources is part of public health monitoring exercises to determine acceptable risk, analyse environmental exposure for risk management and service efficiency diagnosis (Figure 5.1).

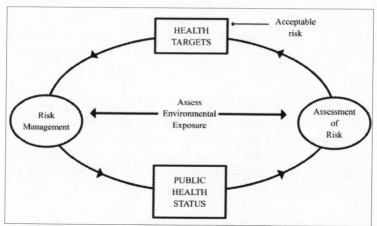

Figure 5.1: Model of Linkages between public health status and assessment of risk in domestic water sources
Source: Ashbolt et al. 2001

Despite the international declaration on water as human right, access to water is still low in Nigeria both in the urban and rural areas. According to the WHO/UNICEF Joint Monitoring Programme, between 1990 and 2004 urban population growth in Nigeria increased from 35 to 48 % while the rural population declined by roughly the same percentage. The same report indicated that urban access to improved water sources actually declined during the same period, from 80 % to 67 % coverage. Rural access to improved water sources also declined during the same

period, by 2 %, still reflecting low levels of coverage at 31% between
1990 and 2004 (WHO and UNICEF, 2010).

The decline in urban water access in Nigeria is striking, but even more
critical is the information not reflected in these numbers. Simplifying
data in this way (urban vs. rural) can mask deep disparities within
metropolitan areas where access to water and sanitation services vary by
geographic location within the city and proximity to the piped
infrastructure, as well as household socioeconomic status. Residences in
blighted areas where land tenure is questionable and with higher
population density are often marginalised in data capturing and policy
interventions (Adeniji, 2008).

The situation of water supply shortages in Ibadan is not different from
other cities in Nigeria. For instance, in 1995, Centre for African
Settlement Studies and Development (CASSAD) reported that only 47
percent of the Ibadan city's population has access to a public water
supply system, 24 percent are reported to draw their water from leaking
pipes and natural springs while 14 percent were through public
boreholes and 9 percent were through hand dug wells.

In order to combat the challenges, the state and the local governments
and local communities in the city came up with adaptation strategies
which were facilitated by the United Nations Development Programme
(UNDP) and the UN-Habitat under the Sustainable Ibadan Project
(SIP). Strategies designed include; the development of mini water
schemes, natural springs and managements of watersheds. In 1995,
about 25 natural springs were identified in different local communities
during the city's consultation forum. At the start-up, Akeu Spring was
developed in 1997, the success of which facilitated the replication in four
other local communities namely, Agbadagbudu (2002), Onipasan (2003),
Sango (2003) and Adegbayi (2004).

The development and use of natural springs by the residents of these benefitting communities have facilitated improved access to water (Itama et al, 2006). Water quality testing is necessary even though lack of education among the people utilising the water source leads them to believe that as long as they are getting water from a source, it is safe. Once a source of water has been provided, adequate attention must be given to quantity and quality of the supply (Awuah et al. 2009). The questions on the quality and portability of water from natural spring sources is what this paper intends to answer by providing the physical, chemical and bacteriological compositions of water from the four natural springs. Water quality determines the 'goodness' of water for particular purposes (Havelaar, 1993). Water quality tests will give information about the health of the waterway. By testing water over a period of time, the changes in the quality of the water can be seen (McCaffrey, 2003). The objective of this study is to examine the quality of water from natural spring sources and to ascertain that, supply is safe for consumption as an alternative to the municipal supply systems in Ibadan city.

5.2. Data and Methods

5.2.1 The study area

The city of Ibadan is one of the largest indigenous urban centres in tropical Africa. Founded in the year 1820 as a war camp, fortunate events have changed the settlement into a big city with an average radius of 30 kilometres (Agbola and Adeniji, 2007)). The city has over 3,000 villages. The population increased rapidly from 627,000 in 1963 to over 3 million in 2004 and about 5 million in 2006 (SIP, 2004, NPC, 2006). At present, the metropolis has 11 Local Government Areas, 5 belong to the city centre while the remaining 6 belong to the peri-urban (Figure 5.2).

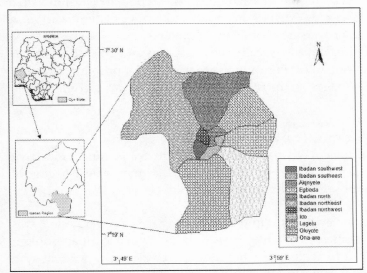

Figure 5.2: Ibadan in the context of Oyo State Nigeria.
Source: Adeniji, 2005

In 1942, the amount of water available to the citizenry was 32 litres per capita per day (LPD). This reduced to 29.6 LPD, 21.7 LPD, 17.4 LPD and 12.5LPD, in 1957, 1965, 1972 and 1995 respectively (NISER, 1995). In 1997, water shortage in the city was such that less than 30 percent of residents were adequately served from the municipal water supply systems (SIP, 2004).

Water Corporation of Oyo State (WCOS) is still the only public agency responsible for the supply and distribution of municipal tap water in Ibadan. Public water supply to Ibadan residents is from two water works (Eleyele, commissioned in 1942 and Asejire, commissioned in 1972). Despite all forms of expansion of the two water works (Eleyele and Asejire) in the past years, the production deficit of 72.8% was recorded (Adeniji, 2008). Agbola and Adeniji (2007) observe that the water shortage problem in the city of Ibadan is much criticised in the indigenous communities and the residential suburbs of most successive immigrants. Ibadan spatial expansions since the construction of Lagos-

Ibadan Express Way in the 70s have no connection to the municipal water systems. The city expands in space and in population without a commensurate improved development of water supply system to serve the population. Inadequate government capacity and misuse of water footprints are among other contributing factors to the problem of public water supply shortages in most Nigerian urban centres (Agbola and Olurin, 2000).

5.2.2 Study Parametres and Methods

Four natural springs (Agbadagbudu, Onipasan, Sango and Adegbayi) which were developed in the second stage of the mini water scheme of the SIP were purposefully selected for the study.

For the water qualitative test, samples of a litre of water per source was collected from each spring with sterile bottles, which contain sodium trioxosulphate and fro-chlorine neutralisation. The samples were kept in an insulated container during transportation between spring sources and the laboratory. They were later transferred into a fridge to maintain the required minimum temperature, which is not conducive for algae growth. Study parametres were determined based on the WHO (1999) water quality indicators and McCaffrey (2003). The parametres include: odour, colour, taste, presence of trace chemicals and bacterial.

The odour was measured by successive dilutions of the sample with odour free water. Turbidio-metree device was used to test for the turbidity (indicates presence of dirt and light transmission) contents in the sample. This is very important in water treatment for aesthetic reasons (WHO, 1991). Total alkalinity titration was carried out to determine the amount of chemical dosages required in the treatment of the spring source.

Chemical test is needful for hygienic assessment in terms of the presence of toxic materials, radioactive elements and other potentially harmful substances (Bartram et al. 2009). Consequently, alkalinity, total hardness, the presence of calcium carbonate and chloride contents of all the spring sources were examined through titration technique.

The test adopted Most Probable Number (MPN) for physical and
chemical analyses (Wolf, 1972) and total coliform count for
bacteriological analysis (total number of pathogen) per 100ml of the
sampled sources (Hendricks 1978). Water qualitative indicators of the
municipal water supply sources (Eleiyele and Asejire) were collected
from the Quality Control Unit of the WCOS.

5.2.3 Inferential data analysis

In order to determine the significance difference between the qualities of
water from the sampled natural springs and the WHO standards for
drinking water, the observed qualitative results were used in comparison
with the state operated municipal water supply sources and the WHO
benchmarks for all the parametres. Bonferroni's Method of ANOVA
was adopted because it provides a comparison of all spring waters
municipal water and with the WHO standard as a control.

"Which spring source of water supply is significantly different from
others, the WHO standards for drinking water and the municipal tap
water?"

The Bonferroni's method provides a pair-wise comparison of the means.
To determine which means are significantly different, we compared all
pairs. There are k = (a) (a-1)/2 possible pairs where a = the number of
treatments. In this example, a= 4, so there are 4(4-1)/2 = 6 pair-wise
differences to consider.0.05 alpha (α) is selected.

In the Bonferroni's method, the idea is to divide this family wise error
rate (0.05) among the k tests. So each test is done at the α/k level. We
use the t distribution to help determine the pair-wise confidence interval.
To start, we need to calculate the pooled variance. This is an estimate of
the variance based on the parametres means. The following equation was
used to determine the pooled variance:

$$S_p^2 = \frac{\sum(n_i - 1)S_i^2}{\sum(n_i - 1)}$$

where n_i is the sample size and s_i is the standard deviation for the sample.

5.3. Results

5.3.1 Physical environment of natural springs

The physical environments of all the four spring locations were examined. Generally, the four springs were developed with simple technology. The adopted design is constructed with local resources. Community members supplied the technocrat skills required during the project execution. Agbadagbudu spring is surrounded by residential houses. The source of the spring is protected with concrete rings, connected with a pipe to drain water into a sump (underground tank) for water storage. The sump is protected with concrete slab with outlet taps serving as water collection points (Figure 5.3).

Figure 5.3: Agbadagbudu natural spring in its environmental setting
Source: Adeniji, 2005

Onipasan spring location is adjacent to a flowing stream (Oloyoro), which is often filled with domestic waste, especially during the rainy season. This is a non-conforming usage because waste water is a potential pollutant which may threaten the spring water quality (Figure 5.4).

Figure 5.4: Onipasan natural spring and the adjoining land uses
Source: Adeniji, 2005

Sango spring is opposite a sawmill refuse disposal site. The site is often set on fire which could create pollution of the underground water through percolation (Figure 5.5). Adegbayi spring is bounded by a mechanic workshop and horticulture garden. Waste from these sites could be dangerous to the spring source, if oil spillage and percolation of organic manure occur (Figure 5.6).

Figure 5.5: Adjoining land uses to Sango natural spring.
Source: Adeniji, 2005

Figure 5.6: Adjoining land uses to Adegbayi natural spring
Source: Adeniji, 2005

5.3.2 Physiognomy Characteristics

Parametres in this category include: appearance; odour; colour; turbidity; pH; and total suspended solids.

Pure water should be clear, colourless and odourless. Zero values of turbidity were obtained for the sampled sources. This shows that the spring water is okay in terms of turbidity (Table 1).All the sampled spring sources were acidic (pH < 7). Agbadagbudu (4.59), Adegbayi (4.10), Onipasan (5.13) and Sango (6.04).

Total Suspended Solid (TSS) refers to residue of water at 103°C (Ashbolt et al. 2001). All the sampled spring sources have values of zero which means that there is no presence of suspended solid substance. Based on the WHO acceptable TSS value of 580 mg/l, the spring water is suitable for consumption.

5.3.3 Bacteriological Characteristics

Bacteriological examination is particularly important because it offers the most logical test for the detection of faecal and potentially dangerous pollutants (Risebro, et al. 2007). It is therefore mostly used to assess safety of drinking water. In the four sampled spring waters, there is the presence of coliform (faecal matters) in Onipasan, Sango and Adegbayi

spring sources. The only spring source that is bacteriological satisfied
and therefore potable is Agbadagbudu source.

The presence of such faecal indicators in a sample of drinking water
denotes that intestinal pathogens could be present, and that the supply is
therefore potentially dangerous to health. The WHO requires clean water
to have coliform value of zero. The higher the number of pathogen
counts in the bacteriological analysis, the more risky such water source
for drinking (Table 5.1). Similarly, sewage from human, animal sources
may contain the causative organisms (pathogen) of many communicable
diseases such as typhoid, dysentery, cholera etc. An examination of cases
of waterborne diseases in the study area could be linked with the
presence of coliforms in the water sources (not as a causative factor, but
as an associate factor).

5.3.4 Chemical Characteristics

Alkalinity of water is the capacity of that water to accept protons. The
alkalinity values obtained for the four springs show a higher level just like
Asejire and Eleyele sources. They are far above the WHO acceptable
value of 0.5 – 1.0 (mg/L). This means that much more dosage of
chemicals is required for the treatment of the sources.

Total Hardness, calcium hardness and calcium ion tests were carried out
to obtain a value for the formation of foams and lader when using the
water for washing. Of the four springs, only Sango spring shows a level
of higher hardness content. The WHO allowable hardness value is 0-120
while it has 130. For this type of temporary hardness, proper boiling
would do the purification. An advanced treatment would be to add
Calcium Hydroxide [$Ca(OH_2)$].

Chloride content gives the level of natural chlorine level in the water
source in order to determine the requirement magnitude/volume for the
chlorination treatment. From the analysis, it is observed that the four
springs have allowable chlorine content. For example, while the WHO
acceptable chlorine content is 200-600, the springs have 60

(Agbadagbudu), 18 (Onipasan), 52 (Adegbayi), and 91 (Sango) chlorine values (Table 5.1).

Table 5.1: Comparisons of Qualitative Characteristic of water in Ibadan (Natural Springs Vs Dam)

Parametres (mg/L)	WCOS Municipal Supply Sources		Natural Spring Sources				WHO Allowable Level
	Asejire	Eleyele	Agbadagbudu	Onipasan	Adegbayi	Sango	
Physical							
Appearance	Clear	Clear	Clear	Clear	Clear	Clear	Clear
Odour	Fishy	Fishy	Unobjectionable	Objectionable	Objectionable	Objectionable	Objectionable
Colour	1.24	0.5	0	0	0	0	5-50 units
Turbidity	5	4.66	0	0	0	0	5-25 units
Total Suspended Solid (TSS)	0	0.15	0	0	0	0	580-1500
PH	7.2	6.8	4.59	5.13	4.7	6.04	7.0 – 8.5
Chemical							
Alkalinity	38	58	20	50	50	65	0.5 – 1.0
Total Hardness	64	84	115	60	45	130	0 – 120
Calcium ion	44	25.6	16	20	6	40	50 – 150
Calcium Hardness	64	64	40	50	15	100	75 – 200
Chloride	17.6	30	60	18	52	91	200 – 600
Bacteriological							
Total Coliforms/100ml	0	0	0	170	330	490	0

Source: Adeniji, 2005

5.3.5 Statistical inferences on difference in quality of spring water and the WHO standards for drinking water

Table 5.2: Variance analysis on water supply quality of natural spring by parametre

Parametres	Sources	Sum of square	Df	Mean square	F	Pr > F
Odour	Between groups	10.5	1	10.5	3	0.1438
	Within group	17.5	5	3.5		
Colour	Between groups	23	3	7.67	4.6	0.121
	Within group	5	3	1.67		
Turbidity	Between groups	22.5	2	11.25	8.18	0.0386*
	Within group	5.5	4	1.37		
TSS	Between groups	13.2	2	6.6	1.78	0.2794
	Within group	14.8	4	3.7		
Alkalinity	Between groups	27.5	5	5.5	11	0.2248
	Within group	0.5	1	0.5		
Calcium hardness	Between groups	27.5	5	5.5	11	0.2248
	Within group	0.5	1	0.5		
Chloride	Between groups	28	6	4.67	-	-
	Within group	0	0			
Calcium ion	Between groups	28	6	4.67	-	-
	Within group	0	0			

Significant at 0.05 alpha level.

Source: Adeniji, 2005

Analysis of variance on the comparison of quality of water from the four natural springs by parametres shows that turbidity indicates a significant difference at the 0.05 alpha level.

Table 5.3: Comparison of natural spring water with WHO indicators and Supplies from WCOS

Natural springs	Observed	Mean Diff	Std. Error	Std. Dev	95% interval		conf. T		df	Pr (T > t)
					Lower	Upper				
Natural spring water with WHO standards										
Agbadagbudu	9	-86.99	63.542	190.62	-233.51	59.53	-1.369		8	0.895
Onipasan	9	-86.59	65.19	195.59	-236.94	63.75	-1.328		8	0.889
Adegbayi	9	-88.31	64.13	192.40	-236.21	59.58	-1.377		8	0.089*
Sango	9	-68.94	65.66	196.99	-220.36	82.48	-1.049		8	0.838
Natural spring water with WCOS (Asejire) supply sources by parametres										
Agbadagbudu	9	-4.16	6.83	20.49	-19.91	11.59	-0.609		8	0.720
Onipasan	9	-3.76	3.37	10.20	-11.54	4.01	-1.117		8	0.852
Adegbayi	9	-5.48	8.28	24.83	-24.57	13.61	-0.662		8	0.737
Sango	9	13.89	8.91	26.74	-6.67	34.44	1.558		8	0.078
Natural spring water with WCOS (Eleiyele) supply sources by parametres										
Agbadagbudu	9	-5.57	6.19	18.58	-19.84	8.7	-0.899		8	0.803
Onipasan	9	-5.18	1.74	5.23	-9.19	-1.15	-2.97		8	0.991
Adegbayi	9	-6.89	6.38	19.14	-21.61	7.82	-1.08		8	0.844
Sango	9	12.48	7.35	22.06	-4.48	29.44	1.69		8	0.064*

Significant at 0.05 alpha level.
Source: Adeniji, 2005

Comparison of qualitative characteristics of water from natural spring
sources with the WHO standards for drinking water, the t test indicates
that only the Adegbayi natural spring shows a significance difference at
0.05 alpha level (T > t). On the other hand, in comparison with the two
municipal water supply sources (Asejire and Eleiyele), Sango natural
spring shows a significant difference (Table 5.3).

5.4. Discussion
From the qualitative analysis as evident in Table 5.1, it is observed that
physical and chemical characteristics of the four springs are within the
WHO allowable concentration. Except for a slight difference for total
hardness of Sango spring water, there is no significant difference
between the municipal water supply (Asejire and Eleiyele) and the four
springs. Although, the sources were protected from whence the water is
piped into underground tanks, the result of this analysis indicates that
infiltration of pollutants and some chemicals could be associated with
both hydrological and anthropological systems in the environs of the
sampled natural spring.

Considering the bacteriological test results, it was observed that only
Agbadagbudu spring with zero value of total coliforms is potable just
like the municipal water supply sources and as recommended by the
WHO standard. Other spring water sources are contaminated with faecal
substances. The observation of the physical environment of the four
sampled springs provided a quick linkup between spring locations and
the presence of potential pollutants from adjoining land uses to
Onipasan, Adegbayi and Sango springs which showed the presence of
bacteriological elements. Going by this qualitative analysis alone, water
from these three spring sources are not acceptable.

The study also shows that some other land uses around the projects
environs are non - conforming to the WHO safety standard for location
of water for domestic use (JMP, 2010). The indiscriminate refuse dump
in the stream channels, are potential risk factors. The waste disposal site
at the Sango area should be relocated because of its resultant risk to the

spring source. The result of this study is similar to Itama et al. (2006) who concluded that alternative water supply sources such as natural spring is potable only when the location is sanitarily certified. The statistical analysis used to determine the significance of difference in qualitative characteristics of the sampled springs, the dams for public taps and the control (WHO standard) shows that three out of the four sampled spring sources shown significant differences in quality.

This study provided an understanding that three spring sources (Sango, Onipasan and Adegbayi) exhibited the presence of coliform and hardness just like the dams (for tap public water system) in Ibadan city. Despite their different locations, the phenomenon can be explained by some other elements such as geological and seasonal variations. Further studies are required to investigate this, mostly by collecting water sampled in different seasons of the year, not just from the collection taps because the observed hardness could also be traced to oxidation in the storage tanks.

The development and use of natural spring to provide water supply for Ibadan residents is a good innovation to combat water supply shortages in the city. In keeping it sustainable, urgent sanitary actions are to be taken by all the stakeholders. The benefitting communities in particular must work hard to build hygienic environment and proper handling of water at household level. In collaboration with the state government, sanitation facilities (public toilet) should be provided in the concerned communities. There is a need for relocation of non-conforming land uses (mechanic workshop, refuse dump site and horticulture site) which are potential sources of pollutants.

In addition, the state and local government must collaborate to provide adequate chlorination and proper introduction of disinfectants to all underground tanks of these natural springs. This should be done periodically (three to four times in a year) with accurate volume of calcium hydrochloride (chlorination). There should also be a Regular bacteriological assessment of the water after each disinfection process is advocated. When these precautions are put in place, it will be needful to investigate the health outcomes of use of natural spring as domestic water source and to find out whether there is a causative relationship between water access and health status of the benefitting communities.

5.5 Conclusion

Assessment of quality of water supply sources is very significant in determining water access and ensuring a sustainable public health in the context of the Millennium Development Goals (MDGs). This study has shown that available natural spring sources in Ibadan are not totally safe for domestic consumption because the quality assessment indicated the presence of coliform and hard chemicals. In comparison with the tap water in the city, the statistical analysis employed in this study provided information on the degree of variance between the control (WHO) benchmarks and the observed qualitative properties of natural springs that are used as alternative domestic water sources in Ibadan.

The result indicated that three out of the four sampled sources, the dams for public tap water system are significantly different from the acceptable WHO standard for drinking water. It is therefore imperative that the sanitary procedure and adequate disinfection exercise should be ensured in order to maximise the benefits of the development of natural spring as an alternative water supply source for thirsting city. Supplies from alternative water sources such as natural spring should satisfy qualitative parametres thereby guaranteeing improved, safe and acceptable water access.

Acknowledgements

The Authors appreciate useful comments from Prof. C.K. Schidra and Mrs. Oloruntoba of the Department of Community Medicine, UCH, Ibadan , Nigeria for the support given during the qualitative analysis of the spring water in their laboratory.

References

Adeniji, G. 2005. Spring water use and management in mega cities of the World. MURP Dissertation, University of Ibadan

Adeniji, G. 2008 Water governance system in the face of environmental change the: Sustainable criteria for urban water management in Nigeria. *Environ-Link 2,* 2.1**,** 16-24.

Agbola, T. and Adeniji, G. 2007 Reducing water stress through the operationalisation of the environmental planning and management (EPM): A Case Study of Natural Springs Development in Ibadan, Nigeria". *Journal of Environmental Technology,* 1.1**,** 356-368.

Agbola, T. and Olurin, T. A. 2000 Social and environmental dimensions of the changing land cover pattern in Ibadan, a hilly indigenous African city". . *Nigerian Journal of Economic and Social Studies,* 42**,** 381-400.

Ashbolt, Nicholas, J., Willie, Grabow, O. K. and Snozzi, M. 2001. Indicators of microbial water quality. *In:* FEWTRELL, L. and BARTRAM, J. (eds.) *Water Quality: Guidelines, Standards and Health.* London: World Health Organisation (WHO).

Awuah, E., Nyarko, K. B., Owusu, P. A. and Osei-Bonsu, K. 2009. Small town water quality. *Desalination,* 248**,** 453-459.

Bartram, J., Corrales, L., Davison, A., Deere, D., Drury, D., Gordon, B., Howard, G., Rinehold, A. and Stevens, M. 2009. *Water safety plan manual: step-by-step risk management for drinking-water suppliers,* Geneva World Health Organisation.

Centre for African Settlement Studies and Development (CASSAD) 1995. Environmental profile of Ibadan metropolitan area. Ibadan: CASSAD and UN-Habitat.

Havelaar, A. H. 1993. *The place of microbiological monitoring in the production of safe drinking water,* Washington, D. C., ILSI Press.

Hendricks, C. W. 1978. Exceptions to the coliform and the fecal coliform tests. *In:* BERG, N. (ed.) *Indicators of Viruses in Water and Food.*Ann Arbor Science.

Itama, E., Olaseha, I. O. and Sridhar, M. K. C. 2006. Springs as supplementary potable water supplies for inner city populations: a case from Ibadan, Nigeria. *Urban Water Journal,,* 3**,** 215-223.

Joint Monitoring Programme (JPM) 2010. Progress on sanitation and drinking water. Geneva and New York: WHO/UNICEF.

McCaffrey, S. 2003. *Factsheet water quality* [Online]. Namoi Catchment Management Authority.

Available: www.waterwatch.nsw.gov.au;www.namoi.cma.nsw.gov.au [Accessed June 22 2009].

National Population Commission (NPC) 1996. Report s on the 1991
National Population Census: Localities Analysis. . Abuja: Federal Office
of Statistics.

Prüss-Üstün, A., Bos, R., Gore, F. and Bartram, J. 2008. *Safer water, better
health: costs, benefits and sustainability of interventions to protect and promote health,*
Geneva, World Health Organisation.

Risebro, H. L., Doria, M. F., Andersson, Y., Medema, G., Osborn, K.,
Schlosser, O. and Hunter, P. R. 2007. Fault tree analysis of the causes of
waterborne outbreaks. *Journal of water and health,* 5 Suppl 1, 1-18.

Sustainable Ibadan Project (SIP) 2004. The SIP Activities Report.
Ibadan: SIP.

United Nations 2009. Report of the independent expert on the issue of
human rights obligations related to access to safe drinking water and
sanitation, Catarina de Albuquerque. *HUMAN RIGHTS COUNCIL,
Twelfth session Agenda item 3* [Online]. [Accessed July 24, 2009].

United Nations Economic Social and Cultural Organisation (UNESCO)
2002. Substantive issues arising in the implementation of the
International Covenant on Economic, Social and Cultural Right. *Twenty-
Ninth Session, Agenda item 3.* Geneva: United Nations.

WHO and UNICEF 2003. Water, sanitation and drainage: Ensuring
better provision with limited resource. *Environment and Urbanisation,* 15.2,
4 - 47.

WHO and UNICEF Joint Monitoring Programme Nigeria. 2010. *Access
To WASH, 2010* [Online]. Available: WASHwatch.org [Accessed
October 2, 2011].

Wolf, H. W. 1972. The coliform count as a measure of water quality. *In:*
MITCHELL (ed.) *Water Pollution Microbiology.* New York,: Wiley-
Interscience.

World Health Organisation (WHO) 1991.*Drinking Water Standard,*
Geneva, WHO.

World Health Organization (WHO) 1999. Creating Healthy Cities in the
21st Century. In Salterthviate, D (Ed), *The EarthScan Reader on Sustainable
Cities:* London: EarthScan. Chapter 6.

World Health Organisation (WHO). 2000. Performance Indicators for water supply and sanitation. 2000 SRC – Google Scholar.[Accessed Jan. 29, 2007].

World Health Organisation (WHO) 2011. Drinking-Water, Sanitation and Health, .*In:* ASSEMBLY, S.-F. W. H. (ed.) *WHA64.24, Agenda item 13.15.* Geneva: WHO.

Zhao, T., Clavero, M., Doyle, M. and Beuchat, L. 1997. Health relevance of the presence of faecal coliforms in iced tea and leaf tea". *Journal of Food Protection,* 60**,** 215-218.

Chapter 6

Combined Constructed Wetlands and Stabilisation Ponds- a Key Ecotechnology for Treating Africa's Wastewater

[9]E. D.O. Ansa, [10]H. J. Lubberding, and [11]H. J. Gijzen

6.1 Introduction

The Millennium Development Goal for environmental sustainability and basic sanitation seeks to integrate the principles of sustainable development into national policies and programmes, and to reverse the losses of environmental resources while reducing by half the proportion of people without sustainable access to safe drinking water and basic sanitation by 2015 (Johannesburg Summit, 2002). While many doubt the attainability of this goal, efforts are nonetheless being made to increase the number of people having access to safe drinking water and basic sanitation in most African countries. This means that more homes are going to access safe and abundant water supply, resulting in the creation of large volumes of wastewater.

Unfortunately in Sub-Saharan Africa (SSA), particularly West Africa, the treatment of wastewater is still a luxury and large portions of untreated wastewater are dumped into water bodies causing further degradation. This calls for the use of efficient and affordable technologies that takes into consideration Africa's peculiar resources such as abundant sunlight,

[9] Council for Scientific and Industrial Research (CSIR) Water Research Institute, Ghana

[10] UNESCO-The Institute for Water Education , Delft, The Netherlands.

[11] UNESCO Regional Science Bureau for Asia and the Pacific, Jakarta, Indonesia.

high plant diversity and availability of low-cost under-utilised 'wastelands'.

The use of ecotechnologies such as natural wastewater treatment systems therefore seems to be an attractive option. Ecotechnologies are treatment systems that utilise the self-adjusting nature of natural ecosystems with little or no human interventions resulting in beneficial outcomes for both humans and the environment (Mitsch and Jorgensen, 1989). For example in eutrophic lakes, the development of algae in certain concentrations can result in significant deaths of *Escherichia coli* (Ansa et al., 2011). *E. coli* is an indicator of the presence of pathogenic bacteria and possible faecal contamination in water bodies.

In SSA, the main potential for re-use of wastewater is crop irrigation, aquaculture and prevention of degradation of inadequate freshwater resources. The greatest challenge in the re-use of wastewater in SSA is the risk of infection with pathogens considering the use of untreated waste water from freshwater bodies by rural communities in this region. Natural wastewater treatment systems such as waste stabilisation ponds (WSP) and constructed wetlands (CW) are not only efficient in pathogen removal but also have additional benefits that justify investment in such technologies. While countries in SSA are yet to take full advantage of this technology, many pilot and field studies have already begun in East and Southern Africa.

The aim of this paper is to show that the use of natural wastewater treatment systems is the most appropriate option for the treatment of municipal wastewater in Africa in terms of performance and cost. It also seeks to underscore the need for policy makers in the West Africa sub-region to invest in research on combined systems of WSPs and CWs so as to adapt this technology to the peculiar socioeconomic and climatic settings of the region.

6.1.1 Natural wastewater treatment systems

Natural wastewater treatment systems are artificially created systems capable of utilising the ecological, biochemical and physical processes involving wetland flora, soils, and their associated macrofauna and

microbial assemblages to assist in treating wastewater. This process may
occur under aerobic, facultative or anaerobic conditions. Common
examples are WSPs and CW. In recent times the use of combined
systems of constructed wetlands (CW) and waste stabilisation ponds
(WSP) with WSP effluent serving as the influent of the CW is fast
gaining ground and this treatment technology could greatly assist in
treating very large volumes of wastewater generated in Africa.

It has been suggested that in determining the appropriateness or the
sustainability of a wastewater treatment technology, the following factors
need to be considered:
- Its robustness while meeting effluent standards
- Its generation of wastes such as sludge and by products such as
  carbon dioxide emissions
- Its capacity for various re-use options as well as environmental
  benefits
- The extent of chemical usage and the degree of environmental
  nuisance it poses
- Its energy source and consumption as well as land and other
  capital requirements (Brix, 1998; Shutes, 2001

In assessing WSPs and CWs as separate systems and as a combined
system, the above factors as well as the limited and peculiar resources
sub-Saharan Africa had been taken into consideration. This can be
grouped into three main categories:

6.1.1.1 Abundant sunshine and optimal temperature conditions

Sunlight enables WSPs to disinfect wastewaters very efficiently without
the need for chemicals or electricity and their associated carbon dioxide
emissions (Shilton et al., 2008) and to some extent the open waters of
FWS-CW. Sunlight in WSPs can directly damage pathogens and
indirectly during the process of photosynthesis. Sunlight also transfers
energy through algae by increasing the environmental pH and dissolved
oxygen concentration; through sensitisers such as high molecular weight
dissolved organic compounds and together with oxygen radicals achieve

inactivation of pathogens in a process known as photo-oxidation (Curtis et al, 1992; Maynard et al, 1999; Davies-colley et al., 2000).

Very warm African climatic conditions occurring throughout the year is ideal for anaerobic decomposition by microorganisms, a pre-treatment necessary for wastewaters with high BOD. This type of wastewaters, classified as high strength sewage according to Metcalf and Eddy (2003), is typical of most cities or rather slums in Sub-Saharan Africa due to the low use of water for flushing the excreta (Awuah, 2006).

6.1.1.2 Highly diverse macrophyte, microbial and invertebrate communities

The presence of algae and highly diverse aquatic flora creates aerobic conditions through the process of photosynthesis in the case of algae while emergent plants transport oxygen down their stems into their root systems where aerobic microorganisms and macro-invertebrates are active in breaking down organic matter. The root mat structure of these aquatic macrophytes also filters off microorganisms and provides large surfaces for metabolic activities of biofilm microorganisms in CWs (Brix, 1997).Roots of aquatic plants are also massive absorbing nutrients in wastewater in CW (Brix, 1997) while duckweed performs a similar function in WSPs (El-Shafai et al., 2007).

6.1.1.3 Cheap labour and land with suitable topography

As nutrients and to some extent pathogens may be absorbed continually onto these aquatic macrophytes, they ought to be periodically harvested for various uses. However the harvesting of these plants can be laborious and the availability of cheap labour makes the technology cheaper. Duckweed for example doubles its biomass every twenty four hours and optimum management of the plant demands daily harvests (Landolt and Kandeler, 1987). Fortunately, labour is extremely cheap, particularly in rural Africa where this technology is needed most. Dependence on wetland vegetations by rural folks for their livelihood had been a very old practice. Cultivation of such vegetation therefore would enhance the income of these rural communities.

The existence of highlands and cheap lands are great advantages in that it enables the construction of large pond systems and treatment beds while enabling a flow regime that do not need a pumping system. Wastewater flow by gravity from uplands onto lowlands and flow rates can be controlled by taps inserted at appropriate points. Low-lying lands, usually referred to as waterlogged lands or 'wastelands', are usually cheaper to buy even in cities and they usually have highly diverse biota suitable for the construction of CW.

6.1.1.4 Treatment efficiencies of natural wastewater treatment systems

With respect to pathogen removal, a key requirement in Sub-Saharan Africa, natural wastewater treatment systems are superior in performance to conventional wastewater treatment systems. Many authors have reported different efficiencies of domestic wastewater treatment due to different operational and environmental conditions. The following summary compares the efficiencies of some natural treatment systems and some conventional treatment systems (Table 6.1).

Table 6.1: Summary of removal efficiencies from selected treatment systems

Treatment technology	Log Removal		
	Bacteria	Helminth eggs	Protozoan cysts
Activated sludge*	0-2	0-2	0-1
Trickling filter*	0-2	0-2	0-1
Aerated lagoon*	1-2	1-3	0-1
WasteStabilisation Ponds	1-6	1-3	1-4
Constructed Wetland			
(SF)	1-4	-	1-2
(SSF)	1-4	-	1-3

*with settling tank. SF: Surface flow constructed wetland; SSF: sub-surface flow constructed wetland.
Source: Mara and Cairncross, 1989; Quinonez-Diaz *et al.*, 2001

6.2. Waste stabilisation ponds (WSPs) and constructed wetlands (CWs) compared

Waste stabilisation ponds and constructed wetlands have various advantages and disadvantages and their choice for wastewater treatment depends mainly on the additional treatment objectives of engineers and planners. Based on their ability to remove organic matter, nutrients, and pathogens as well as their various capital costs, their merits and demerits are summarised in Table 6.2.

6.2.1 Benefits of Combined WSPs and CWs

The use of combined systems of WSPs and CWs expectedly combines the advantages of both systems while eliminating some of the limitations of either system type. Kadlec (2003) mentioned that the use of free water surface constructed wetlands for polishing effluents from ponds is cost effective when land availability is not drastically constrained. Tanner et al. (2005) had also shown that combined systems of WSPs and CWs may provide more consistent effluent quality than either system alone. Below

86

are additional benefits of combined systems and examples of systems being operated in some developing countries with warm climate:

- Greater biological complexity resulting in higher robustness and operational stability (Tanner et al., 2005)
- Low cost and high purification rates (Steinmann et al, 2003)
- Combine systems remove slightly higher amounts of nutrients (useful if discharging into receiving water bodies) (Noumsi et al, 2005)
- Good removal of FC, BOD, SS and nutrients with commercial benefits (Wang et al, 2005).
- Duckweed covered surface prevents mosquito breeding (Awuah, 2006)
- Addition of aesthetic value to a landscape could generate extra income from eco-tourism and wildlife attraction (Denny, 1997; Shutes, 2001)
- Low skilled manpower requirement (Denny, 1997)
- Direct economic benefits include -Fish farming, thatch harvests for roofing, mats etc, sludge as fertiliser (Denny, 1997)
- Erosion protection and flood control functions (Denny, 1997; Shutes, 2001)

Table 6.2: Merits and demerits of waste stabilisation ponds (WSP) and constructed wetlands (CW). FP refer to facultative pond. FWS: Free Water Surface Wetland, SSF: Subsurface Flow Wetland

Characteristics	Waste stabilisation ponds (WSP)	Constructed wetlands (CW)
Land Requirement	With even high land costs required by WSPs, it could still the cheapest option (Arthur, 1983, Mara, 2006).	Use of CW cost effective when land availability is not drastically constrained (Kadlec, 2003)
	Evaporation of water can be countered by use of storage reservoirs.	CW requires 60% more land space than WSP-FP to produce 25mgL-1 BOD, <150mg SSL-1 (Mara, 2006)
	Mosquito breeding problems	FWS CW may have similar problems with mosquito breeding
FC removal efficiency	Disinfection is more efficient in MP pond (1 log) than in SF-CW (0.47 log). (Tanner et al., 2005)	When influent wastewater concentration is high CW acts as a source of pathogen contamination (Ghermandi et al., 2007)
		Good when loading is low (Kadlec, 2003)
BOD removal efficiency	Effluent high in BOD and SS due to algal presence	with lower loadings CW are excellent in BOD removal (Kadlec, 2003)
Nutrient removal efficiency	Relatively poor, but better when macrophytes are present	Good when loading is low (Kadlec, 2003)
Treatment cost (same water quality)	On the basis of land area requirement, performance and capital, O&M cost, WSP FP is to be preferred to secondary SSF CW (Mara, 2006)	

6.2.1.1 Example 1: Bangladesh

In Bangladesh, small duckweed–operated WSP generated enough duckweed used in feeding fish ponds daily, producing an annual fish yield of 12-16 tons ha^{-1} and generating a profit of US$ 2000.00 per year. This compares very favourably against rice production in the same country which is estimated at making a profit of US$ 1,000.00 -1,400.00 ha^{-1}yr^{-1} (Gijzen et al, 2004).

6.2.1.2 Example 2: China
In a study by Wang et al. (2005), removal of faecal coliforms (FC)-
99.97% (<104cfu/L effluent concentration), BOD-87%, TSS-85%,
NH_3-N-55%, Total Phosphorus-52%. Retention time (18-20days), the
plant treated 100, 1000 m^3d^{-1} wastewater and produced 2,030 tonnes of
fish annually. Harvest of duckweed, reed and fish pays for operating and
maintenance costs.

6.2.1.3 Example 3: Malaysia
Putrajaya Wetlands (200 ha) comprising 24 wetland cells is located in an
urban area. The wetland was created to mainly remove agricultural
pollutants coming from upstream, treat storm water and to control
flooding. It helps to treat non-point sources pollutant so as to keep the
receiving lake pure enough for recreational use. The wetland cells
consisted of 27 types of emergent plants for sediment retention, 35
species of herbaceous plants were planted in the marsh area for erosion
control and bank stabilisation, 22 small islands created in open water
with vegetation harbouring birds and other fauna and serves to facilitate
water filtration, as well as ornamental ponds with colourful flower
species to give an aesthetic value to the wetland. All plants were locally
obtained. Nutrient removal by a section of the wetland (comprising 6
wetland cells) was: 82% total nitrogen, 71% nitrate nitrogen and 84%
phosphate. Wetland creates a pleasant landscape, enhancing ecotourism
and attracting wildlife (Shutes, 2001; Sim et al., 2008).

6.2.1.4 Preliminary results: Ghana
A pilot scale system treatment plant consisting of two duckweed
(*Spirodela polyrrhiza*) ponds sandwiched between two algal ponds received
raw domestic wastewater from a holding tank (Figure 1). Two other
pond systems consisting of entire algal ponds and entire duckweed
ponds were operated alongside the hybrid pond to compare its
performance. A total retention time of twenty days was maintained with
an average flow rate of 6.9 x $10^{-3}m^3d^{-1}$ obtained by gravitational force.
Ponds were circular with a depth of 0.3m and a diametre of 0.38m,
monitored at 7.00 -9.00am for 14 months. Duckweed ponds were

harvested once every two weeks and results of monitoring are presented in Table 6.3.

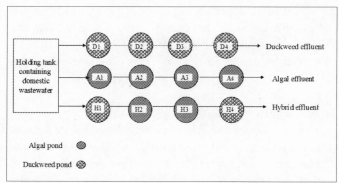

Figure 6.1: Duckweed, algal and hybrid pond systems.

Source: Ansa et al (2012)

Table 6.3: Results of monitoring the treatment systems. Effluent concentrations in bracket

	Duckweed Ponds	Algal Ponds	Hybrid Ponds
BOD (mg/L)	92% (13.5)	73% (45.5)	89% (18.5)
NH3-N (mg/L)	84% (11.6)	86% (19.0)	91% (6.6)
Total Phosphorus (mg/L)	69% (1.7)	49% (2.8)	63% (1.9)
FC (log removal)	3.7 (4.2×10^3)*	4.7 (3.6×10^2)*	4.3 (9.1×10^2)*
Chlorophyll-a Concentration (μgL^{-1})	39	383	76

*FC concentration in cfu/100mL .
Source: Ansa et al (2012)

6.2.2 Economic benefit of duckweed

The economic benefits of duckweed as a result of its high protein content are well documented in literature (Landolt and Kandeler, 1987). The rate of production of duckweed in wastewater treatment system however varies from region to region. It is therefore important that local data is generated for sound financial analysis. In Accra, Ghana, the experimental pilot scale duckweed wastewater treatment plant described above, had a duckweed production rate of $135 gm^{-2}d^{-1}$ fresh weight while in Kumasi, Ghana, a much lower rate of $79.8 gm^{-2}d^{-1}$ fresh weight was observed (Awuah, 2006). This production rate can be increased when daily harvesting of duckweed is practiced instead of harvesting once every two weeks. El Shafai et al. (2007) reported a duckweed production rate of $821.8 gm^{-2}d^{-1}$ in Egypt. It is estimated that even with a modest duckweed production rate of $135 gm^{-2}d^{-1}$ fresh weight and a feed conversion factor of 1 (Cross, 2003), its potential for commercial fish farming as part of an integrated wastewater treatment system is huge.

6.3. Conclusion, challenges and research opportunities

The use of combined systems of WSPs and CWs in an integrated system of wastewater treatment is an efficient and feasible option of converting waste-water into an economic good while achieving treatment guidelines. In inserting duckweed ponds in between algal ponds, concentration of algae in effluent is reduced. Many challenges however exist in adapting this technology in Sub-Saharan Africa. The following areas present excellent areas for research in adapting this technology in sub-Saharan Africa:

- Prevention of clogging of CW when MP effluent serves as influent of CW
- Identifying suitable local plants as filtering macrophytes that are disease resistant and gives optimum performance.
- Local conditions affecting the duckweed production rate.
- Identifying suitable local fish species and fish feed formulations

Acknowledgements

Financial support from Netherlands Government and Government of Ghana is acknowledged.

References

Ansa, E.D.O., Allotey, G.K., Lubberding, H.J., Ampofo, J.A. and Gijzen, H.J. (2012). Performance of a hybrid algal and duckweed pond system treating raw domestic wastewater. Ghana J. Sci 52:3-16

Ansa, E. D. O., Lubberding, H. J., Ampofo, J. A. and Gijzen, H. J. 2011.The role of algae in the removal of Escherichia coli in a tropical eutrophic lake. *Ecological Engineering,* 37, 317-324.

Arthur, J. P. 1983. Notes on the design and operation of waste stabilisation ponds in warm climates of developing countries. Washington, DC: The World Bank,.

Awuah, E. 2006.*Pathogen removal mechanisms in macrophyte and algal waste stabilisation ponds.* PhD, Wageningen University/UNESCO-IHE.

Brix, H. 1997. Do macrophytes play a role in constructed treatment wetlands? .*Water Science and Technology,* 35, 11-17.

Brix, H. How 'green' are constructed wetland treatment systems? *In:* TAUK-TORNISIELO, M., ed. 6th International conference on wetland systems for water pollution control, 1998 Brazil. Brazil Ecological Society.

Cross, J. W. 2003. Duckweed as a primary feedstock for aquaculture: A summary of its potential advantages., . Available: http://www.mobot.org/jwcross/duckweed/Fish.htm [Accessed October 25,2011].

Curtis, T. P., Mara, D. D. and Silva, S. A. 1992. Influence of pH, Oxygen, and Humic Substances on Ability of Sunlight To Damage Fecal Coliforms in Waste Stabilisation Pond Water. *Applied and environmental microbiology,* 58, 1335-43.

Davies-Colley, R. J., Donnison, A. M. and Speed, D. J. 2000.Towards a mechanistic understanding of pond disinfection.*Water Science and Technology,* 42(10-11), 149-158.

Denny, P. 1997.Implementation of constructed wetlands in developing countries.*Water Science and Technology,* 35, 27-34.

El-Shafai, S. A., El-Gohary, F. A., Nasr, F. A., van der Steen, N. P. and
Gijzen, H. J. 2007.Nutrient recovery from domestic wastewater using a
UASB-duckweed ponds system. *Bioresource technology,* 98, 798-807.

Garcia, M., Soto, F., Gonzalez, J. M. and Becares, E. 2008. A
comparison of bacterial removal efficiencies in constructed wetlands and
algae-based systems. *Ecological Engineering,* 32, 238-243.

Ghermandi, A., Bixio, D., Traverso, P., Cersosimo, I. and Thoeye, C.
2007. The removal of pathogens in surface-flow constructed wetlands
and its implications for water reuse. *Water science and technology* 56, 207-16.

Johannesburg Summit. Report of the world summit on sustainable
development Johannesburg Summit, 2002 Johannesburg, South Africa.

Kadlec, R. H. 2003. Pond and wetland treatment. *Water science and
technology: a journal of the International Association on Water Pollution Research,*
48, 1-8.

Landolt, E. and Kandeler, R. 1987. *Phytochemistry, physiology, application and
bibliography., Biosystematic investigations in the family of duckweeds (Lemnaceae),*
Zurich Geobotanischen Instutites der ETH Stiftung Rubel

Mara, D. and Cairncross, S. 1989. Guidelines for the safe use of
wastewater and excreta in agriculture and aquaculture, .Geneva World
Health Organisation.

Mara, D. D. 2006. Constructed wetlands and waste stabilisation ponds
for small rural communities in the United Kingdom: A comparison of
land area requirements, performance and costs. . *Environmental Technology*
27, 753-757.

Maynard, H. E., Ouki, S. K. and Williams, S. C. 1999. Tertiary lagoons: A
review of removal mechanisms and performance. *Water Research,* 33, 1-
13.

Metcalf, L. and Eddy, H. P. 2003.*Wastewater Engineering: Treatment,
Disposal, Reuse,* New York, McGray-Hill New.

Mitsch, W. J. and Jorgensen, S. E. 1989.*Ecological engineering: an introduction
to ecotechnology. ,* New York, USA., Wiley and Sons

Moussa, M. S., Rojas, A. R., Hooijmans, C. M., Gijzen, H. J. and van
Loosdrecht, M. C. M. 2004. Model-based evaluation of nitrogen removal
in a tannery wastewater treatment plant. *Water science and technology: a
journal of the International Association on Water Pollution Research,* 50, 251-60.

Noumsi, I.M.K, Nya, J., Akoa,A, Eteme, R.A., Ndikefor, A., Fonkou,T. and Brissaud, E. (2005). Microphyte and macrophyte-based lagooning in tropical regions. Water Sci. Technol. 51(12): 267-274

Quinonez-Diaz, M. J., Karpiscak, M., Ellman, E. D. and Gerba, C. P. 2001. Removal of pathogenic and indicator microoganisms by a constructed wetland receiving untreated domestic wastewater. *Journal of Environmental Science and Health,* A36, 1311-1320.

Shilton, A. N., Mara, D. D., Craggs, R. and Powell, N. 2008. Solar-powered aeration and disinfection, anaerobic co-digestion, biological CO2 scrubbing and biofuel production: the energy and carbon management opportunities of waste stabilisation ponds. *Water science and technology : a journal of the International Association on Water Pollution Research,* 58, 253-8.

Shutes, R. B. 2001. Artificial wetlands and water quality improvement. *Environment international,* 26, 441-7.

Sim, C. H., Yusoff, M. K., Shutes, B., Ho, S. C. and Mansor, M. 2008. Nutrient removal in a pilot and full scale constructed wetland, Putrajaya city, Malaysia. *Journal of environmental management,* 88, 307-17.

Steinmann, C. R., Weinhart, S. and Melzer, A. 2003. A combined system of lagoon and constructed wetland for an effective wastewater treatment. *Water research,* 37, 2035-42.

Tanner, C. C., Craggs, R. J., Sukias, J. P. S. and Park, J. B. K. 2005. Comparison of maturation ponds and constructed wetlands as the final stage of an advanced pond system. *Water science and technology : a journal of the International Association on Water Pollution Research,* 51, 307-14.

Wang, L., Peng, J., Wang, B. and Cao, R. 2005. Performance of a combined eco-system of ponds and constructed wetlands for wastewater reclamation and reuse. *Water science and technology : a journal of the International Association on Water Pollution Research,* 51, 315-23.

Chapter 7

Estimates of Wastewater Generation and use in Urban Ghana

[12]S. K. Agodzo and [13]F. P Huibers

7.1. Introduction

Ghana (4^0 44'N and 11^0 15'N; 3^0 15'W and 1^0 12'E), located on the west coast of Africa, occupies an area of about 24 million ha with the population figure now reaching 24.23 million according to the 2010 population and housing census (Table 7.1). Population growth rate averages 2.5 % for the period 2000 -2010. Due to the increasing world population and the consequent demand for more water for several uses, the world's consensus is that future wars are not likely to be fought because of oil or other precious minerals but rather because of water (Agodzo *et al*, 2001). Consequently, demand for water has increased with the resultant generation of wastewater.

At the present levels of technology, wastewater treatment and reuse is common in many countries because of increased demand for water. Where the wastewater is untreated or partially treated, other beneficial uses are found in such water. This includes urban and peri-urban irrigation. Despite the economic gains and benefits to the farmer and the state, there are also costs. If not well organised, the health costs may be high. If organised well, there are costs of wastewater storage and delivery that must be recovered. Where the wastewater is treated, there are costs involved not only in improving the quality of water but also in the

---

[12] Agricultural Engineering Department, Kwame Nkrumah University of Science and Technology, Ghana

[13] Irrigation and Water Engineering Chair Group, Wageningen University, The Netherlands

storage and delivery, depending on the distance between the treatment plant and the farm (Pescod, 1992). Costs are calculated differently and done subjectively by different people (Mastenbroek, 2001).

Table 7.1: Provisional figures of the 2010 population and housing census in Ghana

Region	Population		Inter-census % increase[a]	Inter-census % growth rate[a]
	2010	2000		
Western	2,325,597	1,924,577	20.8	1.9
Central	2,107,209	1,593,823	32.2	2.8
Greater Accra	3,909,764	2,905,726	34.6	3.0
Volta	2,099,876	1,635,421	28.4	2.5
Eastern	2,596,013	2,106,696	23.2	2.1
Ashanti	4,725,046	3,612,950	30.8	2.7
Brong Ahafo	2,282,128	1,815,408	25.7	2.3
Northern	2,468,557	1,820,806	35.6	3.1
Upper East	1,031,478	920,089	12.1	1.1
Upper West	677,763	576,583	17.5	1.6
Ghana	24,233,431	18,912,079	28.1	2.5

Source: Ghana Statistical Service (2011); [a]Author's estimate (2011)

The use of wastewater, whether raw or untreated, may not be socially desirable due to the odour, the nuisance and social attitudes but may be socially tolerated as long as there are beneficial uses for it especially when it can be used to generate economic activity and support livelihoods. This paper examines the potentials of wastewater use in Ghana under the broader issues of urban water supply and sanitation, current use of wastewater (treated + untreated) and the costs of wastewater pollution.

7.2. Water Supply Facilities

In 1986, the Ghana Water and Sewage Corporation (GWSC), now Ghana Water Company Limited (GWCL), operated 194 pipe-borne water supply systems of which 103 including larger urban systems, utilise river flow and 91 using groundwater (GWSC, 1986). In 2000, the GWCL operated and maintained 208 pipe-borne systems, serving 70% of the urban population and about 6,500 hand pump/borehole systems also serving about 50 % of the rural population. Of the 208 pipe-borne systems, 122 serve urban communities while the remaining 86 serve the rural communities. About 70 % of the supply capacity serves the urban communities in Accra-Tema, Kumasi and Sekondi-Takoradi, which constituted about 43 % of the total population receiving or enjoying piped water (GWCL, 2000).

Under the Community Water and Sanitation Agency (CWSA), communities are to own, operate and manage their water supply systems. The Agency is to facilitate the development, monitoring and management of the systems. Even though the emphasis has been on the provision of small pipe systems, most of the rural systems are boreholes fitted with pumps. GWCL is increasingly facing difficulties in operating and maintaining water supply and sewage facilities because of: (i) severe shortage of experienced and properly trained professionals and technical manpower at all organisational levels; (ii) frequent breakdowns of machinery and equipment as a result of lack of adequate routine and preventive maintenance, inadequate and untimely importation of essential spares, chemicals and other supplies, backlog in timely replacement of worn-out equipment, rising cost of fuel, lubricants and materials, and shortage of roadworthy and reliable fleet of vehicles and the poor condition of roads; and (iii) delays in the completion of on-going projects, resulting in high cost overruns and prolonged retention of labour force that could be used for other purposes. All these problems were further compounded by: (i) delays in adjusting the tariff structure to rising costs and difficulties in the prompt payment of bills by consumers; and (ii) delays in the disbursement of both investment and operational subsidies committed by the Government.

With less government interference in price regulation of public utilities, the approval of new water rates by the Public Utilities Regulatory Commission (PURC) was anticipated to improve considerably the financial situation of the company and to inject fresh capital into the improvement of facilities and general services. There was also speculation of privatisation of the water sector in order to inject capital and expertise into the sector. Even though the GWCL has put in place a comprehensive recovery plan for its physical assets as well as its organisation in order to provide reliable services to its consumers, it is still not able to raise the needed capital from its operations to fund such plans.

The urban water supply systems usually operate at a very low efficiency. The water transmission efficiency has been often below 50 %, meaning that the transmission losses were and are still high. These might be due to the old age of equipment, pipe leakage, unauthorised connections and sometimes inadequate capacity of the GWCL to detect problems and respond to reported problems on the pipe lines (Agodzo *et al.*, 2003).

7.3 Wastewater Disposal and Treatment Systems in Ghana
In Ghana, collection and disposal of domestic wastewater is done using:
- Underground tanks such as septic tanks and aqua-privies either at industrial houses or at community facilities and then transported by de-sludging tankers to treatment works or dumping sites. The transportation is done by the waste management department of the district/municipal/metropolitan assemblies and some private tanker owners, police, the army etc.
- sewerage systems

Domestic wastewater in addition to storm water in the cities, also discharge into the main drains that end up in nearby water bodies. Some of the urban dwellers discharge their faecal waste into septic tanks while the kitchen and other waste from the home are directed into the nearest open drains. In the slums of Accra and Kumasi for example, where housing is done haphazardly, the drainage systems are woefully inadequate, quite often posing health problems to the inhabitants. In the well-planned and laid-out housing estates in the cities, drainage facilities are better but not always adequate to cope with effluents and storm water. Because drainage system costs are usually prohibitive, the majority of the urban drains are open drains, which lend themselves to misuse, sometimes serving as defecating points for households that do not have adequate sanitation facilities (Agodzo *et al.*, 2003). Since the 1990s, there have been a number of estate development activities concentrated mainly in the peri-urban areas of Accra and Tema but wastewater disposal systems employed in these areas have been largely underground septic tanks.

Two of the country's three major communities' water-carriage sewage systems are in Accra under GWCL, and in Tema, by the Tema Development Corporation (TDC). Tahal Consulting Engineers Limited and Engineering Science Incorporated in 1965 prepared a master plan for both systems. Less than 300 connections were made to the Accra Sewage Systems (ASS), which was due to the fact that the main sewers so far constructed, were located in high density, own-income commercial and office areas. The major problem of the ASS was the broken sea outfall, which posed a serious health risk. The present plan calls for a diversion of the sewage to the oxidation ponds for pre-treatment before disposal into the sea. There will also be improvements and some additions to the present systems, according to the master plan.

The Tema Sewage System (TSS) is much more extensive and comprehensive than the Accra system, and works reasonably satisfactorily, although maintenance of the pumping plants leaves much to be desired. According to Benjamin (2001), the TSS had 20,000m^3/day capacity but the volume of liquid waste generated was about 1,525 m^3/day. Sewer services were charged by the Tema Development Corporation (TDC), amounting to about US $ 3.50 per household per annum.

Industrial wastewater in Ghana is discharged from the breweries and such industries as the textile, mining, chemical and pharmaceutical industries. These liquid wastes are usually discharged into the drains without any pre-treatment. Under the current regulations of the

Environmental Protection Agency (EPA) of Ghana, industrial waste must be pre-treated before disposal.

7.3.1 Wastewater treatment facilities

The main types of treatment facilities used in Ghana are oxidation or waste stabilisation ponds, aerated lagoons, trickling filter and activated sludge process treatment facilities. All the wastewater treatment facilities in the country are used for treating domestic wastewater (Ministry of Works and Housing, 1998).

As at 1978, there were about 30 sewage treatment plants in Ghana but there are hardly any data on them. The majority of the treatment facilities are located in the Greater-Accra region. The rest are scattered almost evenly throughout the regions. In Accra, the wastewater treatment facilities available are under the control of institutions such as the Ministry of Defence (Burma Camp, 37 Military Hospital, Military Academy and Training School) and the Public Works Department (Government Ministries, Korle-Bu Hospital, Mental Hospital, Educational Institutions: University of Ghana, Achimota School, Accra High School) Accra Metropolitan Assembly (AMA) has four faecal sludge treatment plants under its jurisdiction. They are used for septage and night soil treatment. The four plants include Achimota Faecal Plant (250 m3/day dumping rate), Korle Gonno Faecal Plant/ Polate Sewage Plant (50 m3/day), Teshie-Nungua Faecal Plant (80 m3/day). Most faecal sludge and sewage treatment plants are in poor operating conditions.

7.3.1.1 The Korle lagoon wastewater treatment plant

A modern biological treatment plant (UASB wastewater treatment plant) designed by LeAF (the Netherlands) and constructed and in operational transfer by TaySec (England) to the Accra Metropolitan Assembly (AMA) uses low energy and requires minimum maintenance. Treating combined wastewater from domestic and industrial sources, the system has a design influent flow rate of about 15,600 m3/day, but currently it receives an average of 2500-6000 m3/day. According to Hyde and Hyde (2002), the influent characteristics vary as shown by some of the physical, chemical and biological parametres: $3.0 < pH < 12.5$; $80,000 < BOD < 90,000$ mg/l; $COD < 150,000$ mg/l. These parametres have large diurnal and seasonal variations. After treatment, the effluent BOD and TSS range between 17-19 mg/l and 20-22 mg/l respectively. While the climate is ideal for the biological treatment process, small pumps requiring low energy are used to pump at the various stages of the treatment process.

7.3.2 Domestic wastewater generation

The wastewater flow estimates (based on procedures in Box 7.1) for urban Ghana and the 10 regional capitals of Ghana shown in Tables 2 and 3 are based on assumed per capita water consumption rates. In 2000, total urban wastewater generated for the year could reach 278.7 million m^3 and that for the 10 regional capitals 178.3 million m^3 for the same year. That is, the regional capitals alone could generate as much as 64 % of the potentially generated wastewater within the year. Projected into 2020, urban Ghana could generate as much as 763.4 million m^3 and the 10 regional capitals 405.8 million m^3 annually.

Box 7. 1: Estimation of wastewater flow

The value of wastewater flow used for sewer design is the daily peak flow. This can be estimated as follows (Mara, Sleigh and Tayler, 2001):

$$q = k_1 \, k_2 w p / 86400 \tag{1}$$

where   q = daily peak flow (l/s)

k_1 = peak factor (= daily peak flow divided by average daily flow)

k_2 = return factor (= wastewater flow divided by water consumption)

w = average water consumption (litres per person per day)

P = population served by sewer (projected population)

A suitable design value for k_1 for simplified sewage is 1.8 and k_2 may be taken as 0.85 based on peri-urban areas of Brazil but the k_2 values could range between 0.65 for low income areas to 0.95 in areas where water supply is by public standpipes (Mara, Sleigh and Tayler, 2001). The average daily flow can be estimated as the peak daily flow divided by the peak factor. For this study, estimates in Ghana (Tables 7.2 and 7.3) will be based on the assumptions above, assuming k_1 and k_2 values as 1.8 and 0.8 respectively. Considering that urban population in Ghana is 5000 and above, daily average water consumption for 2000 and 2020 are assumed as 76 and 91 l/person/day respectively.

Projected population (P) is calculated using the formula:

$$P = P_i \, (1 + r)^n \tag{2}$$

Where P_i = initial population

r = population growth rate

n = number of years

Table 7.2: Urban wastewater generation estimates

Year	2000	2020
Ghana's population	18,412,247	30,170,610
% Urbanisation[1]	37.9	52.9
Urban population	6,978,242	15,960,253
Urban water demand (m³/day)	530,346	1,452,383
Urban wastewater generation (m³/day)[2]	763,698	2,091,432

Source: Ministry of Works and Housing (1998). Agodzo et al (2003).

For design purposes, urban effluent also includes storm water into drains.

7.3.3 Estimates of potential wastewater irrigation for urban Ghana

Out of the estimated 278.8 million m^3 (2000 figure) and 763.4 million m^3 (2020 figure) of wastewater that can be generated in urban Ghana, if only 10 % is used for irrigation in the urban/peri-urban centres at an irrigation water requirement of 600 mm per annum, the total area that could be irrigated using waste water in the year 2000 and 2020 could be up to 4,600 and 12,720 ha respectively. For an average farm size per farmer as 0.5 ha, this could provide a livelihood for about 9,200 and 25,440 farmers in the urban areas of Ghana for 2000 and 2020 respectively. It will be practically impossible to recover all the wastewater for irrigation purposes in the urban centres and the technological interventions to do this could be expensive. Assuming an average farm income of $ 1,400/ha/annum (estimated from Cornish and Aidoo, 2000), the total income that can be generated in 2000 and 2020 based on the above analysis, using only 10 % of the potentially generated urban wastewater could be $ 6.44 million and $ 17.8 million per annum respectively.

103

Table 7.3: Wastewater flow estimates for the regional capitals in Ghana

Urban Area	Population			WWF (l/s)	Estimate	Annual WWF Estimate (10^6 m³)	
	2000[a]	2010[b]	2020[b]	2000	2020	2000	2020
Accra	1,657,913	2,550,156	3,922,579	2,100	5,949	66.2	187.6
Kumasi	1,017,246	1,314,921	1,699,704	1,287	2,578	40.6	81.2
Sekondi-Takoradi	359,298	478,199	636,447	454	965	14.4	30.4
Sunyani	179,267	231,726	299,535	228	454	7.2	14.4
Koforidua	139,370	160,136	183,968	207	279	5.6	8.8
Cape Coast	119,340	145,475	177,333	177	269	4.8	8.5
Tamale	300,931	400,517	533,058	382	808	12.1	25.5
Ho	233,514	279,120	333,633	295	505	9.4	16.0
Bolgatanga	225,864	251,976	281,106	287	426	9.1	13.4
Wa	224,467	265,682	314,465	284	475	8.9	15.0
Total for Regional Capitals and their corresponding districts						178.3	405.8
Urban Ghana						278.7	763.4
% Waste water generated by regional capitals compared to urban Ghana						64.0	53.2

Source: Agodzo et al (2003); [a]Ghana Statistical Service (GSS) provisional figures, [b]estimates; WWF = wastewater flow; the population figures cover metropolitan, municipal and district boundaries and not necessarily the township boundaries only.

7.3.4 The cost of wastewater pollution and who pays

There is no formula for passing on the cost of cleaning the environment in Ghana. Whereas the cost of pollution may still not feature in the current Ghanaian economic analysis, it will be a matter of time when the issues will be considered more seriously. In this study, a useful example of the polluter paying the cost of cleaning up the environment will be adopted (Box 7.2): Following from the presentation in Box 7.2, the wastewater charge in Ghana is computed based on equation 3 in the box. The following assumptions are made:

- An average household in the urban centres should have 5 and 4 people in 2000 and 2020 respectively. As individual property ownership increases, there will be less number of people per household.
- The flat rate tax (T) per household per annum for polluting the environment is assumed as US $ 2.00 and US $ 3.50 for 2000 and 2020 respectively.
- The average water consumption per household per annum is 130 m^3 for 2000 and 156 m^3 for 2020.
- The social compensation factors for 2000 and 2020 are assumed as 0.6 and 0.7 respectively.

The total wastewater pollution charges summarised in Table 7.5 suggest that in a year (2000), Accra, Kumasi and urban Ghana alone should be able to raise revenues as pollution taxes totalling about US $ 1.3 million, US $ 0.8 million and US $ 5.4 million respectively.

Projected into 2020 these values for Accra, Kumasi and urban Ghana for one year could rise to US $ 9.4 million, US $ 4.1 million and US $ 38.1 million respectively. These monies can be channelled into urban sewer system improvement and waste treatment projects. Urban/peri-urban irrigation projects can even be financed from these pollution taxes.

Box 7. 2: Formula for computing wastewater fee (van Humbeeck, 2000)

"Households in the Flanders region in Belgium every year pay fees for both drinking and wastewater. Residents pay the wastewater charge to the Flemish government, which uses it to finance environmental programs The drinking water fee goes to 1 of 24 private water companies in Flanders, which use the money to pay for drinking water production (Van Humbeeck, 1997). A social correction, in the form of a pricing formula to help low-income and large families pay for wastewater, has always accompanied the wastewater charge. In 1997, however, the government replaced this approach with a tax exemption for certain underprivileged groups. The reform created a new formula to calculate the drinking water fee. Households with water connections now receive 15m3 of drinking water per person per year for free. To determine the wastewater charge, the government calculates a household's pollution load with a pollution conversion coefficient. The basic tax formula looks like this:

$$H = T .OC .Q \qquad (1)$$

where, H is the tax amount that is due; T is the flat tax rate (US $16 in 1991-95; US $ 24 in 1996-99); OC is the conversion coefficient that is applied for domestic wastewater effluents (0.025); and Q is the water consumption expressed in m^3. The government, however, has always amended this basic formula with a social correction factor. In 1991 it exempted the first 30 m^3 of water consumed per household from charges. This was applied to all households. The reasoning was that low-income households would consume less, and thus the exemption would proportionally benefit them the most. Furthermore, it reduced the charges by US $ 6.75 per child for couples with three or more children, starting with the third child. In other words, it calculated the 1991 charge by applying the following formula:

$$H = T .OC.(Q - 30) - 250 .(k-2) \qquad (2)$$

where, k is the number of children (for k>2).

Because of administrative difficulties with implementing these measures, the government introduced a different social compensation scheme in 1992. It multiplied the charge by a social compensation factor, Ks, that varied from 0.20 to 0.95, depending on the volume of water consumption. Hence, until 1996 it calculated the tax amount as follows:

$$H = T .OC .Q .Ks \qquad (3)$$

where, Ks depends on the volume of water consumed, Ks = Ks(Q)

Table 7.1: Social compensation factor Ks as a function of water consumption

Q (m³)	0-50	51-100	101-150	151-200	201-300	301-400	401-500
Ks	0.20	0.40	0.60	0.70	0.85	0.90	0.95

It was soon realised that this scheme also did not work well. Despite the increasing block rate, the lowest income groups paid substantially more taxes than higher income groups as a percentage of total income. Moreover, the plan placed a proportionately heavier burden on larger households (Decoster and Van Dongen, 1994; SERV, 1993; Van Humbeeck, 1997). Several alternatives were proposed but the government hesitated to change the formula. Finally, the government abolished the Ks factors in 1997. Instead, it introduced a tax exemption for certain underprivileged groups: elderly tax payers who receive welfare money, and disabled residents who receive a government allowance. For non-exempt households it used a formula corresponding with equation 1 to calculate the wastewater charge. To compensate for the abolition of the Ks factors in wastewater charge, the government passed a new regulation: beginning in 1997, the water companies had to supply all household customers with 15 m3 of drinking water per person per year."

Table 7.4: Proposed wastewater pollution charges for urban Ghana

Urban Area	Number of Households, N		Q (m³/year)		OC	Ks		T (US$/year)		H=N.T.Q.OC.Ks (US$/year)	
	2000	2020	2000	2020		2000	2020	2000	2020	2000	2020
Accra	331583	980645	130	156	0.025	0.6	0.7	2.0	3.5	1293174	9370063
Kumasi	203449	424926	130	156	0.025	0.6	0.7	2.0	3.5	793451	4060168
Urban Ghana	1395648	3990064	130	156	0.025	0.6	0.7	2.0	3.5	5443027	38125062

Source: Agodzo et al (2003); Q = annual water consumption per household.

7.4. Future considerations

Some future interventions proposed under the African Development Bank – funded Africa Water Facility (AWF) project including pilot plants located in Greater-Accra, Sekondi-Takoradi and Kumasi will progressively transfer the "design for reuse" model to other cities in Ghana and Africa at large. The project will also train local engineers and planners to employ a reuse-oriented planning process for the design and implementation of future wastewater and faecal sludge treatment, with intended benefits as urban irrigation (Box 3.3).

Box 7.3: Wastewater re-use as part of the African Water Facility Project (AfDB, 2011)

Under what was known as the DANIDA B2B-programme, a Danish technology biological wastewater treatment system was introduced in Ghana as a partnership between thirteen (13) Danish companies and more than 50 Ghanaian companies which took part in the first Tech Change Fair and Match Making event in Ghana from 24-26 March, 2009. Companies from the environment, energy and agro business sectors took part in the event. The idea of the partnership is to introduce "plug-and-play" wastewater treatment units in Ghana for single housing units up to 10,000 person units. Earlier, the first wastewater treatment unit was installed at the Kofi Annan International Peacekeeping Training Centre (KAIPCT) in Accra. The unit is treating the wastewater from the Centre's staff and trainees. Treated wastewater is reused for gardening and car wash. The project at the KAIPCT has proven the technology locally and is forming a showcase for the partnership, when introducing potential customers to the technology.

The Ghanaian Government did set 2009 as the target date for all wastewater to be treated and subjected to the norms that regulate the discharge of industrial wastewater into the sewage systems, lakes, rivers and the ocean with compliance estimates of 90.8% by 2010. The Government of Ghana received a Loan from International Development Association (IDA) and the fund had been budgeted for building nine (9) water and wastewater treatment in Accra, Kumasi, Takoradi and Asamankese. Among services required by the GoG were COB/BOD reduction, odour control and water re-utilisation systems for industrial and agricultural use.

7.5. Conclusion

There is the need to dispose of wastewater *safely* and *beneficially* (Pescod, 1992): safely, because we need to be conscious of our environmental health, such as disease and even nuisance; beneficially, because the growing pressure on such resources as water requires that we develop new technologies to reuse wastewater either in a treated, partially-treated or raw form. The beneficial uses of wastewater include urban agriculture, urban greening and even car washing. Most of urban Ghana does not have the required infrastructure to manage wastewater and the costs of putting in place the required infrastructure to effectively collect and dispose of all urban wastewater will be prohibitive.

It will simply be a matter of time for Ghana to move to such levels of development where urban wastewater can be discharged at logical points and safely. Accra, for example, is known to be flooded almost every year because of the choking of the open drains. The present situation does however raise issues of environmental concern with health implications. The other option is to attempt to find beneficial uses of such wastewater in the context of urban and peri-urban agriculture (Agodzo *et al*, 2003).

Even though there are no byelaws (except those of the Accra Metropolitan Assembly) prohibiting the use of urban wastewater for agriculture, there are no such laws promoting the activity either. There is always a conflict between urban agriculture and city modernisation probably due to the notion that agriculture does not really belong to the city but is a rural activity. The farmers do not really have any land title rights and always have to give up their lands to the city authorities in the name of modernisation. The environmental concerns of hygiene and the consequent health implications of using contaminated water and eating contaminated vegetables by the consuming public have been much talked about in most of the literature that has something to do with urban and peri-urban agriculture. However, balancing environmental law enforcement with the promotion of urban agriculture that sustains livelihoods and reduces urban poverty has not been easy (Agodzo *et al*, 2003).

There are also costs of polluting the environment. In other words, everyone who discharges some form of waste into the environment, whether liquid or solid, has some responsibility to pay for the cleaning up of the environment. But in Ghana, the issue has not even come up for discussion, let alone for laws to be enacted to make the polluter pay for cleaning up the environment. Finding beneficial uses of liquid waste in urban agriculture, which will require putting in place a certain basic infrastructure to clean up the waste and safely dispose of it, will require some level of commitment on the part of the city authorities who must be prepared to see this as part of city planning and development (Agodzo *et al*, 2003).

Acknowledgements

The authors wish to express appreciation to the W4F – Wastewater Project of the Wageningen University, Netherlands for funding part of the study.

References

AfDB. 2011. Two Africa water facilities launched in Ghana. African Development Bank Group. Available at: http://www.afdb.org/en/news-and-events/ghana/. Accessed 2/11/11

Agodzo, S., Huibers, F., Chenini, F., van Lier, J. and Duran, A. 2003. Use of wastewater in irrigated agriculture. Country studies from Bolivia, Ghana and Tunisia. . *W4F-Wastewater.* Wageningen: WUR.

Agodzo, S. K., Huibers, F. P., Chenini, F. and Maldonado, P. Use of treated wastewater for irrigated agriculture proposals for a comparative study of Bolivia, Ghana and Tunisia. *In:* DZISI, A. K. and AGODZO, S. K., eds. First School of Engineering Research Retreat SERR1 25-26 September 2001 Obuasi School of Engineering, KNUST,, pp15.

Benjamin, L. T. 2001. Personal communications. Waste management Division, Tema Development Corporation (TDC), Tema, Ghana

Cornish G. A. and Aidoo, J. B. 2000. Informal irrigation in the peri urban zone of Kumasi, Ghana. HR Wallingford/KNUST/DFID KAR Project Report OD/TN97.

Decoster, A. and Dogen, H. 1994.Verdelingseffecten van milieuheffingen *in* VERBRUGGEN, A. (ed.) *Milieu-en Natuurrapport Vlaanderen* Mechelen, Belgium: Flemish Society for the Environment.

Ghana Statistical Service (GSS) 2001.2000 population and housing census.Provisional Results. Accra: Ghana Statistical Service.

Ghana Statistical Service (GSS) 2011.2010 population and housing census.Provisional Results. Accra: Ghana Statistical Service

Ghana Water and Sewerage Corporation (GWSC) now GWCL 1986. Five year rehabilitation and development plan. Accra, Ghana: Ghana Water and Sewerage Corporation.

Ghana Water Company Limited (GWCL) 2000. Water Sector Development Report. Accra: Ghana Water Company Limited.

Hyde, R. and Hyde, K. 2002. *RE: Personal communications by site engineer and site chemist.* AMA, Accra. TaySec/Korle Lagoon Treatment Plant

Mara, D., Sleigh, A. and Tayler, K. 2001. PC-based simplified sewer design. DFID /University of Leeds

Mastenbroek, A. 2001. *Treated wastewater pricing: calculating costs or a political decision making process?* MSc, Wageningen University.

Ministry of Works and Housing 1998. Ghana water resources management challenges and opportunities *Water Resources Management Study* Ministry of Works and Housing

Pescod, M. 1992. Wastewater treatment and use in agriculture. *FAO Irrigation and Drainage Paper* Rome: FAO.

Sociaal-Economische Raad van Vlaanderen or Social and Economic Council of Flanders (SERV) 1993. Advies over de Sociale Correctie met betrekking tot de Heffing op de Verontreiniging van de Oppervlaktewateren. Brussels.

Van Humbeeck, P. 1997. Environmental Taxation in Flanders. *Environmental Taxation and Accounting,* 1, 52-61.

Van Humbeeck, P. 2000. *The distributive effects of water price reform on households in the Flanders Region of Belgium*, Oxford University Press.

Appendix: Summary of the Development and Use of Natural Springs in Ibadan

S/N	ACTIVITIES	NATURAL SPRING LOCATIONS			
1.	Physical features of the Project	Agbadagbudu	Onipasan	Adegbayi	Sango
	Project Land Area (m²)	645.0	265.2	176.107	509.63
	Types of Drainage	Open	Close	Open	Open
	Accessible route to the location	Foot path	Access Road	Express road	Access road
	Adjoining land uses	Residential, Church, and a Mosque	Residential, Stream & Mechanic Workshop.	Mechanic Workshop and Horticulture garden	Residential, Saw mill Refuse Disposal site
	Number of overhead tanks	-	Two	-	Two
2.	Patronage of the Project				
	Population of the Benefiting Communities	60,171	13,594	6 284	58,706
	Service Radius (Km²)	3	3.270	2.12	2.97
	Average No of Users per day	250	275	120	400
	Average volume of consumption per Household (A_1)	150 litres	150 litres	180 litres	120 litres
	Volume of consumption per person/day (A_2)	25 litres	25 litres	30 litres	22.5 litres
3.	Water Quality in comparison with the WHO standard				
	Locality	Not potentially hazardous	Potentially hazardous	Potentially hazardous	Potentially hazardous
	Physical test	Within the WHO standard	Within the WHO standard	Within the WHO standard	Within the WHO standard
	Chemical test	Acceptable	Acceptable	Acceptable	Acceptable
	Bacteriological test	Not conformed	Not conformed	Not conformed	Not conformed
	Disinfection process	Not adequate	Not available	Not available	Not available
	Sanitation facilities	Public toilet	-	Improved pit latrine	Public Toilet

Chapter 8

The Land Rush in Africa: Implications and Institutional Panacea

[14]Evans S .Osabuohien,[15]Adeyemi Ogundipe and [16]Uchenna R. Efobi

8.1 Introduction

Land is that part of the earth that is not covered by water and is one of the most relevant natural resources. This is given the fact that it plays host to economic resources such as mineral, forest and other valuable resources. Land also provides the basis for most agricultural operations such as planting, irrigation and a host of others. Above all, modern activities such as transportation, construction of buildings, schools and hospitals require land. This has made the demand for land to always be on the increase.

On the reverse, the supply of land is fixed. Given the increase in its usage and relatively inelastic supply, the market for land cannot be perfect. With the rising population, agricultural land hectares (ha) area per capita has witnessed a continuous decline within the period 1961 to 2008 (Oxfam International, 2011).

In this wise, when land is not available in the required acreage in a given location, acquisition elsewhere becomes the option. Thus, the issue of large scale Foreign Land Acquisitions (FLAs) or land grabbing comes to bear (Brüntrup, 2011).Land deal can be generally defined as deals/acquisitions involving outright purchases and lease of land areas over 1000 ha (Cotula *et al.*, 2009). It can range into several millions of ha

---

[14] Department of Economics & Development Studies, Covenant University, Nigeria

[15] Department of Economics & Development Studies, Covenant University, Nigeria

[16] Department of Accounting, Covenant University, Nigeria

and the duration for the lease can be as much as 100 years. Thus, FLAs can be conceptualised as the purchase/lease of land by individuals and entities outside their country of origin.

The paper is motivated essentially by the increasing FLAs in African countries, as have been reported in recent years. One of the driving forces for FLAs in Africa can be attributed to the presumed availability of cheap lands. Africa and Latin America are said to have about 80% of world reserves of agricultural land with Angola, Democratic Republic of Congo (DRC) and Sudan being among the seven countries that account for about half of the world land reserve (IFPRI, 2009).

Some of the major reasons for the increasing reports of FLAs include: boom for bio-fuel policies induced by the governments especially in European Union, United States and Brazil; rising food prices (crisis) in the world market especially between 2007 and 2011; the global financial crises of 2007/2008, which made investors to seek for alternative source of investment to reduce the effects of financial market volatility; increasing oil price that resulted in seeking for alternative bio-mass, which led to the use of bio-based material; the sale of certificate for reducing emissions; and increasing specialisation for rising land prices (Cotula, *et al.*, 2009; Brüntrup, 2011; Deininger *et al.*, 2011). The above can be categorised as: agro-fuels, carbon trade, food supply, and other alternative investments (Land Portal, 2011).

Cases of FLAs have been reported across the world; however, developing countries especially those in Africa attract a large proportion of FLAs as a result of some perceived benefits of their governments. These include: access to favourable conditions for capital; access to better markets; investment in infrastructures; access to knowledge, technologies and management; agricultural production for internal markets; employment creation; and more sources of taxes and levies (Cotula, *et al.*, 2009; Brüntrup, 2011). Another similar reason is the quest for water as it has been noted that the Middle Eastern States are among the biggest land investors in Africa, which are driven not by sufficiency of land but of water (Oxfam International, 2011).

In addition to the above, it has been reported that lands in Sub- Saharan Africa (SSA) are the cheapest compared to other places in the world. For example, land in Zambia, which is the most expensive in SSA is only 12.5% the price of similar land in Argentina or Brazil, and less than 5% of that in Germany (Oxfam International, 2011). In this regard, a critical driving interest for LSFLAs in Africa is investors' anticipated high returns.

FLAs have some implications, which can be far-reaching. This is particularly interesting for African countries where there are difficulties in feeding their rising population. For instance, food accounts for about 46% of an average household's total spending in West Africa and some countries-e.g. Mali account for about 53 % (Oxfam International, 2011). Another implication is the displacement of small-scale farmers from their major means of livelihood (agriculture), therefore leading to a poor livelihood in the long-run.

Potential adverse effects on the environment may also occur due to large-scale fertiliser and chemical applications, which has the risk of reducing agricultural production in the host countries (FAO-IFAD-UNCTAD-The World Bank Group, 2011). The impact of this can be gruesome as a greater proportion of African population (over 70% in some countries) dwell in the rural areas where their major livelihood depends on land for agricultural purposes (Cutola et al., 2009). Furthermore, some of the FLAs possess the land for securing valuable natural resources at the expense of the livelihood of the rural dwellers (Modie, 2011).

The above threats from FLAs are imperative due to the fact that many African countries have poor legal and procedural mechanisms to protect local rights; livelihoods and welfare of citizens. Even when there are such mechanisms, the processes of community consultation in the negotiation of the FLAs are almost non-existent and in some cases, private gains supersede the demand of land owners. This can be attributed to lack of transparency, inadequate checks and balances in contract negotiations resulting from corruption, which can lead to land deals that do not represent the public interest (Cotula *et al.*, 2009).

In this wise, many governments in developing countries corruptly offer a large portion of land at ridiculously cheap prices and investors cashing in to maximise return. In some instances citizens 'wake up' to hear of FLAs made by their government without their input. Therefore, this paper examines the reason and implications of FLAs in Africa with regards to agricultural export and food security.

8.2. Institutions and Foreign Land Acquisition

The metaphor "good institutions, better economic development", can be situated in the light of foreign land deals. This is because the institutional quality has been noted to play important role in managing economic affairs. The seminal work of the North fostered this idea, following the fact that it is becoming increasingly obvious that economic agents engaged in economic transactions are influenced principally by institutions among others (Natal, 2001; Meon and Sekkat, 2008; Osabuohien, 2011; *Osabuohien and Ike, 2011).*

Institutions include humanly formulated mechanisms that have some measure of control of individuals in economic and social activities. It consists of an informal (sanctions, taboos, customs, and traditions governing the way of life of a group of persons) and formal institutions-constitutions, laws, and decrees (North, 1991; *Williamson, 2000;* Acemoglu and Johnson, 2005; Acemoglu and Robinson, 2008). Institutions are put in place to create a peaceful habitation, reduce uncertainty in exchange of economic values, and reduce the possibility of moral hazards and adverse selections.

The quality of institutions in a country can create choices that can affect transactions and production costs. More so, institutions matter as they create policies in an economy that will be relevant for securing property rights. This is in agreement with the development and efficient use of resources for economic growth and development (Cavalcanti *et al.*, 2008). In other words, inappropriate institutional arrangements and policies in a country can lead to sub-optimal economic performance (Temple, 1999).

Relating this with land deals in Africa, land governance and deals will depend to a considerable extent, on the prevailing institutional quality in the concerned countries. This is based on the LaPorta *et al.,* (1999) and Natal (2001) backdrop that economic activities engaged by individuals can be determined by some social and legal relationships existing among them. In this wise, the available institution in a country will define the procedures to be followed in land acquisition and enforce the implementation of same.

The nature of the negotiation processes and the level of consultations (coverage of interests to be represented in the deal) will be determined, to a large extent, by the political leaders in the host countries. These leaders may sometime join alliance with the local community leaders where such transactions will be made and by so, extract rent from the land deals. Sometimes, the stance to be eventually taken by these leaders, in the negotiation process, will be guarded by the extent of economic rents that can be gotten from the foreign investors. It has been reported that land investors make promises to the host communities and do not keep to them because the institutional framework to enforce compliance are not adequately provided for in the country. As a result of this, land investors target mainly countries that have a weak institutional framework to promote their 'trade'. (Cotula *et al.,* 2011; Deininger *et al.,* 2011; Oxfam International, 2011).

Anseeuw *et al.,* (2012a) puts this in context by emphasising that there are four key failures of governance that brings about adverse consequences from LSFLDs. They observe that weak democratisation in the form of deficit accountability and transparency will contribute to elite capture of lands. The development of the legal system was also emphasised as a poor legal structure that will translate into poor property right protection and unjust dispossession of ancestral lands.

Taking this further, this study presents a framework showing the role of institutions in cushioning the extent and effect of foreign land acquisitions on land owners. From Figure 1, the household uses their ancestral lands for the agricultural purposes. This debases the notion that

FLAs target idle lands (Anseeuw *et al.*, 2012a). Land owners use these lands for the cultivation of agricultural crops either for subsistence or commercialisation. In some cases when these lands are not being used for agricultural purpose, the government can intervene to engage community in agricultural outfits and with this, the lands are efficient being used. In the event of land rush, foreign investors will desire these lands because they are fertile and can be used for agricultural production. As Anseeuw *et al.*, (2012b) noted, these investors are targeting crop lands or crop vegetation mosaic, which account for about 45 % of the total land deals in Africa. This is denoted by the straight line arrow flowing from household, ancestral land and foreign investors (Figure 8.1).

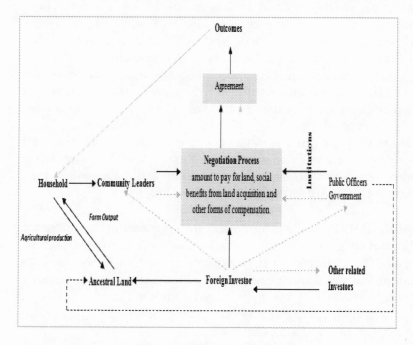

Figure 8.1: Institutions and impact of LSFLDs
Source: Authors' 2012

As the demand for the land, and negotiation process begins, the household who owns the land may not have the capacity for the negotiations process and mostly make use of the community leaders.

These community leaders convey the desires of the household to the investors and at the same time act as an intermediary between the investors and the household. At this point, the role of public institutions is emphasised. This is based on their contributions to making policies that will regulate the negotiation processes such as land rights, private property protections and the likes and also, ensure that these policies are adhered to.

At this point, a smooth negotiation process that upholds the desires of the land owners will be ensured. This is denoted by the straight line running from foreign investor, community leader and public officers via institutions to the negotiation process. From this process, agreement will be reached and then the outcome from such agreement will be beneficial to the household. This is denoted with the straight line from the negotiation process to the agreement and then the outcome. It is worth observing that a straight line runs from the outcome of the agreement to the household. This implies that when favourable agreements are reached from the negotiation process, foreign investors will uphold to such agreements, which will reflect in the livelihood of the household land owners. This is based on the strength of the institution and the commitment of public officers to ensure the realisation of the agreements.

On the contrary, foreign investors can liaise with community leaders and public officers to enter into agreement for private gains. This is denoted by the broken faint lines, running from foreign investor to community leaders and public officers. In Figure 8.1, it can be observed that the input of public officers flows in the negotiation process below institutions and policies. This implies that when foreign investors are able to cajole public officers with incentives and gains, then institutions in the form of policies and regulations are not brought to bear during the negotiation process. They negotiate neglecting the policies and guidelines that protect land owners. This goes for traditional leaders, who neglect the strong opinions of the household during the negotiation process. This is also denoted by the broken faint arrow. At this point, agreements are reached but such agreements do not translate into outcomes. Hence, no favourable positive effect on the household livelihood.

This position is in congruence with Anseuuw *et al.*, (2012a and b) who noted that foreign land investors target countries with poor institutional infrastructure. By this, they are able to find their way around policies and acquire more land. The broken and direct arrow flowing from/to foreign investor to/from other related investors signify a feedback mechanism that propels land rush.

To take this further, this study selects 16 countries in Africa where the issue of foreign land deals has been reported. These countries include: Angola, Cameroon, Democratic Republic of Congo (DRC), Egypt, Ethiopia, Ghana, Kenya, Madagascar, Malawi, Mali, Mozambique, Nigeria, Sierra Leone, Sudan, Tanzania and Zambia. The study analysed the availability of land to agricultural production using the period average 1996 - 2000, 2001-2005, 2006 - 2010, with the aim of establishing the extent of land rush during the periods of media report (2006 - 2009) as observed by IFPRI, (2009) and Land Portal, (2011). Given the role of governance and institutions in this discourse, the study also brought to bear the data on institutional quality using some indicators from Kaufmann *et al.*,(2010)

8.2.1 Land and Institutions in the Selected Countries
The study began the descriptive analysis by establishing the dependence of these countries on agriculture using the mean values of trends in agricultural export (*agrex*), food export (*foodx*) and food import (*foodm*) during the period 1995 - 2008 and reported in Figure 8.2.

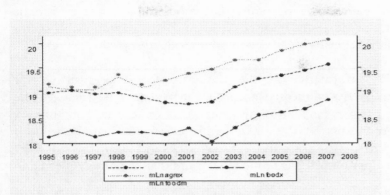

Figure 8.2: Trend in agricultural and food export in selected countries (Authors' computation using World Bank data (2011)

Note: Logarithmic transformed values were used to show the rate of change and make them more comparable.

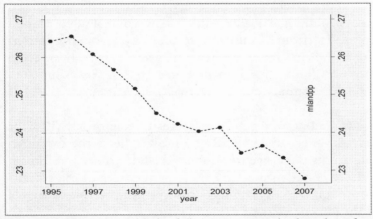

Figure 8.3: Trend in arable land (ha) per persons in the selected countries
Source: Authors' computation using World Bank (2011)

As shown in Figure 8.2, the variables had upward trends; however, agricultural and food exports exhibited some fluctuations. The crucial observation that can be made is that the food import was consistently above food export throughout the period. This indicates that the selected countries are increasingly becoming net food importers. This can be attributed among others to poor government participation in this sector and land insufficiency to boost agricultural productivity.

Figure 8.3 is informative as the trajectory for land available for agricultural purposes witnessed a consistent decline. The trend of the arable land ha per persons shows that the value has continuously declined over the period 1995-2008. Another issue is that the value is less than 0.5 ha per persons and between 1995 and 2007; the value for arable land ha per person has reduced by more than 200% as reflected in Figure 8.3.

Having established the declining trend in agricultural land availability and the marginal production from agricultural activities, the study went further to examine the relative institutional qualities of these countries. We compared the institutional performance of these countries with the average values for SSA. This is intended to observe institutional qualities of the selected countries, relative to the average value for SSA. We used three measures of institutional quality—rule of law, control of corruption and regulatory quality from Kaufmann *et al.* data set on institutions across countries. Their rating index values ranged from -2.5 (worst/weak) to +2.5 (best/strong) institutional quality. (See Kaufmann *et al.*, 2010 for details regarding world governance indicators).

Table 8.1 presents, among others, the measures of rule of law (RL) for the 16 sampled countries of Africa. Rule of law reflects the extent to which economic agents (inclusive of household land owners and foreign land investors) have confidence in and abide by the rules of the society. This includes the quality of contract enforcement, property rights protection and the effectiveness of the legal systems.

Table 8.1: Rule of Law (RL) in the Selected Countries and SSA Average

	1996	1998	2000	2002	2004	2006	2008	2010
Calculated Version for RL								
SSA	-0.75	-0.73	-0.72	-0.71	-0.77	-0.73	-0.74	-0.74
Average of 16	*-0.91*	-0.93	-0.86	-0.84	-0.80	-0.78	-0.74	-0.77
Angola	-1.60	-1.57	-1.62	-1.46	-1.34	-1.25	-1.28	-1.24
Cameroun	-1.44	-1.15	-1.16	-1.16	-1.14	-1.01	-0.99	-1.04
DRC	-1.95	-2.11	-2.01	-1.87	-1.82	-1.79	-1.68	-1.61
Egypt	0.08	-0.06	-0.03	-0.02	0.05	-0.15	-0.09	-0.11
Ethiopia	-0.84	-0.72	-0.82	-0.79	-0.69	-0.56	-0.60	-0.76
Ghana	-0.32	-0.44	-0.03	-0.11	-0.24	-0.02	-0.10	-0.07
Kenya	-0.98	-1.11	-0.96	-1.00	-0.89	-0.89	-0.98	-1.01
Madagascar	-0.63	-0.69	-0.32	-0.23	-0.14	-0.41	-0.46	-0.84
Malawi	-0.41	-0.56	-0.57	-0.66	-0.42	-0.53	-0.29	-0.14
Mali	-0.50	-0.51	-0.47	-0.38	-0.28	-0.40	-0.35	-0.46
Mozambique	-0.83	-0.91	-0.81	-0.75	-0.75	-0.70	-0.66	-0.50
Nigeria	-1.19	-1.30	-1.14	-1.45	-1.50	-1.14	-1.12	-1.21
Sierra Leone	-1.49	-1.18	-1.38	-1.33	-1.10	-1.16	-1.03	-0.94
Sudan	-1.60	-1.57	-1.46	-1.24	-1.52	-1.35	-1.50	-1.32
Tanzania	-0.21	-0.37	-0.42	-0.46	-0.40	-0.46	-0.28	-0.51
Zambia	-0.63	-0.58	-0.55	-0.49	-0.58	-0.63	-0.50	-0.49

Note: -2.5 = worst/weak, +2.5 = best/strong.
Source: Authors' compilation/computation using data from Kaufmann *et al.*, (2010)

From Table 8.1, SSA countries performed poorly, considering that the RL values ranged from 0.71 to -0.77. Similarly, the sampled countries performed even worse as they had a lower values ranging from -0.77 to 0.93.

During the period, some countries had scored as low as -2.11 and 2.01. Considering that the countries had negative values for most of the period apart from Egypt that had positive scores in both 1996 and 2004. It will be rational to conclude that these countries' legal systems are not efficient to foster the protection of private properties and ensure qualitative contract terms especially in the case of foreign land acquisition. Many of the countries performed below the SSA average over the period except a few countries such as Egypt, Ghana, Malawi, Mali, Tanzania and Zambia.

Taking this further, the extent of the countries control of corruption (CC) was investigated and the trend reported in Table 8.2. The measure CC reveals the extent to which public power is exercised for private gain and the extent of elitist 'capture' of the state for private interests. As reflected in the model (Figure 8.1), the lower this value, the easier it is for foreign investors to relent in their responsibilities since they are able to influence community leaders and public officers with private gains. The statistics from Table 8.2 reveals that in SSA, the extent of corruption and elitist capture still remains high. This is based on the statistics that range from -0.58 to -0.67.

Table 8.2: Corruption in the Selected Countries and SSA Average

	1996	1998	2000	2002	2004	2006	2008	2010
				Calculated Version for CC				
SSA	-0.59	-0.63	-0.58	-0.59	-0.67	-0.64	-0.62	-0.60
Average of 16	-0.81	-0.87	-0.83	-0.83	-0.83	-0.78	-0.75	-0.73
Angola	-1.16	-1.39	-1.55	-1.21	-1.31	-1.19	-1.22	-1.33
Cameroun	-1.16	-1.22	-1.03	-1.10	-1.08	-1.03	-0.90	-0.98
DRC	-2.06	-1.81	-1.71	-1.53	-1.44	-1.51	-1.31	-1.38
Egypt	-0.07	-0.28	-0.40	-0.33	-0.46	-0.52	-0.67	-0.56

Ethiopia	-1.16	-0.55	-0.45	-0.50	-0.72	-0.65	-0.66	-0.70
Ghana	-0.22	-0.31	-0.16	-0.32	-0.27	-0.03	-0.06	0.09
Kenya	-1.03	-1.13	-1.00	-1.02	-0.87	-0.89	-1.01	-0.91
Madagascar	0.20	-0.42	-0.05	0.13	-0.12	-0.25	-0.10	-0.27
Malawi	-0.22	-0.36	-0.37	-0.97	-0.76	-0.73	-0.59	-0.42
Mali	-0.44	-0.62	-0.64	-0.38	-0.37	-0.44	-0.47	-0.68
Mozambique	-0.36	-0.71	-0.68	-0.72	-0.74	-0.66	-0.55	-0.40
Nigeria	-1.16	-1.17	-1.25	-1.47	-1.36	-1.19	-0.92	-0.99
Sierra Leone	-0.78	-0.94	-0.93	-0.80	-0.88	-1.12	-1.07	-0.76
Sudan	-1.28	-1.00	-0.93	-1.02	-1.31	-1.17	-1.49	-1.33
Tanzania	-1.03	-1.12	-1.11	-1.01	-0.67	-0.40	-0.51	-0.49
Zambia	-1.03	-0.92	-0.94	-0.98	-0.86	-0.74	-0.48	-0.57

Source: Authors' compilation/computation using Data from Kaufmann *et al.*, (2010)

The average value for the sampled countries is also disheartening as they remain in the lower pedestal to SSA. Most of them had lower controls of corruption as they had values below the SSA average. Very few such countries like Egypt, Ghana, Madagascar, Malawi and Mali had values higher than the SSA average in most of the periods studied. However, their values were negative. This becomes an issue as households and landowners suffer by the dispossession of their ancestral lands to foreign investors, with poor benefits, because of corrupt practices of public officers and traditional leaders.

In congruence with the statistics, Jacques (2012) observed that land acquisitions in Africa are cascaded by corruption due to the weakness of the government institution responsible for the enforcement of proper contractual agreements. This is the case in most parts of Africa where the government and other public officers engage in land contracts with foreigners with the intention of self- actualisation. The Shonga case in Nigeria, where the government was accused of selling land to

Zimbabwean farmers for personal gains, is a case in point. Cotula (2011) and Aabo and Kring, (2012) emphasised that lack of transparency is prevalent in most of the land deal processes in African countries.

The role of the government is emphasised at this point. This is because a responsive government will be required to curtail excesses of economic agents. In this case, the activities of foreign investors in communities where land is acquired can be checked by an effective government regulation and monitoring. Furthermore, in cases where foreign investors are not able to meet up with the terms of their agreements, the government is supposed to take adequate measures to ensure the attainment of such agreements. The paradox is that most governments in countries where FLAs is prevalent are not responsive to the needs of the citizens.

The quality of policies formulated by the government and the implementation of same for the promotion of private sector development can reduce the consequences of FLAs. In cases where there is poor regulatory quality, the issue of unfair dealing comes to be, because there are no adequate institutions to regulate the excesses of economic agents when dealing with related parties. In Table 8.3, the value of the regulatory quality for SSA was negative in all the periods. Similar reflection is observed from the values of the individual countries. Most of the countries had negative values for most of the period. This signifies that in these countries, there are poor policies to promote efficient private sector development.

Table 8.3: Regulatory quality in the selected countries and SSA average

	1996	1998	2000	2002	2004	2006	2008	2010
SSA	-0.75	-0.71	-0.67	-0.68	-0.74	-0.73	-0.74	-0.71
Average of 16	-0.84	-0.79	-0.72	-0.80	-0.74	-0.68	-0.64	-0.64
Angola	-1.45	-1.72	-1.82	-1.48	-1.25	-1.14	-1.06	-1.05
Cameroun	-1.13	-0.64	-0.60	-0.89	-0.66	-0.86	-0.83	-0.72

DRC	-1.83	-2.41	-2.11	-1.51	-1.59	-1.32	-1.30	-1.60
Egypt	0.01	-0.34	-0.35	-0.50	-0.49	-0.42	-0.18	-0.18
Ethiopia	-1.34	-1.18	-1.16	-1.23	-0.96	-0.95	-0.83	-0.88
Ghana	-0.38	-0.24	-0.09	-0.46	-0.34	-0.06	-0.02	0.09
Kenya	-0.37	-0.34	-0.30	-0.20	-0.28	-0.26	-0.24	-0.13
Madagascar	-1.05	-0.82	-0.46	-0.28	-0.32	-0.19	-0.32	-0.59
Malawi	-0.29	-0.23	-0.22	-0.47	-0.51	-0.45	-0.48	-0.57
Mali	-0.48	-0.24	-0.12	-0.44	-0.45	-0.41	-0.40	-0.47
Mozambique	-0.54	-0.29	-0.17	-0.30	-0.46	-0.52	-0.47	-0.37
Nigeria	-0.83	-0.93	-0.75	-1.26	-1.34	-0.91	-0.78	-0.78
Sierra Leone	-1.61	-1.33	-1.39	-1.27	-1.00	-1.17	-0.97	-0.72
Sudan	-1.37	-1.36	-1.44	-1.29	-1.17	-1.21	-1.47	-1.36
Tanzania	-0.42	-0.41	-0.25	-0.56	-0.45	-0.31	-0.50	-0.41
Zambia	-0.42	-0.12	-0.27	-0.62	-0.53	-0.65	-0.45	-0.49

Source: Authors' compilation/computation using Data from World Governance Indicator (2011).

The issue of land grabbing and the attendant severe consequences on the household and community cannot be resolved without sound regulatory qualities. In some cases, where lands are taken over for exploitation, land degradation and pollution become paramount and with poor regulatory qualities as observed in Table 3, the communities suffer. Some of these consequences include pollution of the water source accessible to the communities, air pollution bringing about organic mutations and the likes. However, the government responsiveness becomes cardinal.

The above seems to suggest that the governments in selected countries will be easily influenced and when policies are developed, the political will to ensure the adherence to such policies will be lacking. Therefore, the intense extent of the 'mad' land rush in these countries is not too surprising. From the foregoing, this study has been able to articulate that institutional quality matters to the extent of foreign land acquisition in Africa.

8.3. Policy Consideration

The issue of institutional quality cannot be over emphasised. Statistics have shown that most of the countries where FLAs are prevalent lack strong institutions to regulate and enforce the proper contractual agreement. More so, going beyond contractual agreement to realisation of outcomes that will be yielding to the community require sound institutions.

In this case, this study recommends that both formal and informal institutions be strengthened to recognise the rights of landowners. This will make contractual agreements more inclusive other than few traditional rulers taking decisions on behalf of land owners. This will debase the notion that some lands 'are idle' and decisions ought to be made on behalf of the owners. These lands are ancestral lands, where household derives their livelihood. Therefore a more transparent and inclusive negotiation process will reduce the tendency for corrupt practices.

African governments should be more effective in ensuring that agreements reached during negotiation processes are adhered to. This calls for better government effectiveness in driving foreign investors to be more attentive to the realisation of agreements reached. This has a ripple effect as the livelihood of dispossessed household members depends on the realisation of negotiated agreements. Therefore, there is the need for strengthening the institutional framework especially the promotion of reliable legal and procedural mechanism in order to protect local rights and take into cognisance the aspirations of ancestral land owners.

Acknowledgements

The authors appreciate the useful comments from the anonymous reviewer. The travel grant for participation at International Conference on Sustainable Development of Natural Resources in Africa, Accra, Ghana, 5-8th December, 2011 from the United

Nations University-Institute for Natural Resource in Africa (UNU-INRA) where the first draft of this paper was presented is acknowledged.

This work draws some insights from the first author's postdoctoral research with funding from Alexander von Humboldt Foundation; hence, he appreciates assistance from his hosts (Jann Lay, Leibniz Institute for Global and Area Studies-GIGA and Michael Brüntrup, German Development Institute-DIE).

References

Aabo, E. and Kring, T. 2012. The political economy of large-scale agricultural land acquisitions: implications for food security and livelihoods/employment creation in rural Mozambique. *United Nations Development Programme Working Paper.* United Nations Development Programme.

Acemoglu, D. and Johnson, S. 2005. Unbundling institutions. *Journal of Political Economy,,* 113, 949-995.

Acemoglu, D. and Robinson, J. 2008. The role of institutions. *Commission on Growth and Development Working Paper.*

Anseeuw, W., Boche, M., Breu, T., Giger, M., Lay, J., Messerli, P. and Nolte, K. 2012a. The State of Large-Scale Land Acquisitions in the 'Global South: Analytical report based on the land matrix database'. Hamburg: CDE/CIRAD/GIGA, Bern/Montpeller.

Anseeuw, W., Wily, L., Cotula, L. and Taylor, M. 2012b. Land rights and the rush for land: findings of the global commercial pressures on land research project. Rome: International Land Coalition.

Bank, W. 2011. Africa Development Indicators, Washington DC, The World Bank.

Brüntrup, M. 2011. Detrimental land grabbing or growth poles: determinants and potential development effects of foreign direct land investments. Bonn: German Development Institute.

Cavalcanti, T. V., Magalhaes, A. M. and Tavares, J. A. 2008. Institutions and economic development in Brazil. *The Quarterly journal of economics and finance,* 48 412-432.

Cotula, L. 2011. *Land deals in Africa: What is in the contracts?'* London (UK), International Institute for Environment (IIED).

Cotula, L., Vermeulen, S., Leonard, R. and Keeley, J. 2009. Land grab or development opportunity: Agricultural investment and international land deals in Africa. London/Rome: IIED/FAO/IFAD.

Deininger, K., Byerlee, D., Lindsay, J., Norton, A., Selod, H. and Stickler., M. 2011. Rising global interest in farmland. Washington DC: The World Bank.

FAO/IFAD/UNCTAD 2010. Principles for responsible agricultural investment that respects rights, livelihoods and resources (Extended Version).The World Bank Group.

International Food POLICY Research Institute (IFPRI) 2009. *IFPRI Policy Brief.* International Food POLICY Research Institute.

Jacques, B. 2012. *Massive irresponsible lease of African farm land threatens Africa* [Online]. Available: http://www.afjn.org/focus-campaigns/other/other-continental-issues/161-agriculture/ 1100-massive-irresponsible-lease-of-african-farm-land-threatens-africa.html.

Kaufmann, D., Kraay, A. and Mastruzzi, M. 2010. Governance Matters Viii: Aggregate and Individual Governance Indicators 1996-2010. *World Bank policy research working paper.*

LaPorta, R., Lopez-de-Silanes, F., Shleifer, A. and Vishny, R. 1999. The quality of government.*The journal of law, economics and organisation,* 15, 222-279.

Meon, P. and Sekkat, K. 2008. Institutional quality and trade: which institutions, which trade. *Economic Inquiry,* 46, 227-240.

Modie, A. 2011. Universities must halt land grab investments' [Online]. Available: http://www.universityworldnews.com/article.php?story=062512292. [Accessed 11/04/2012].

Natal, A. 2001. The new institutional economics: a general introduction' *Decocumento De Disscusion Sobre El Neuvo Institucionalismo,* 1, pp.4-21.

North, D. C. 1991. Institutions'. *The Journal of Economic Perspectives, ,* 5, pp. 97-112.

Osabuohien, E. S. 2011. *Analysis of international trade performance in selected SSA countries: the impact of institutional framework.* PhD, Covenant University.

Osabuohien, E. S. and Ike, D. N. 2011. Economic transformation and institutional framework in Nigeria-lessons from Botswana and South Korea. *2011 Annual Conference of Nigerian Economic Society,.*

Oxfam International 2011. Growing a better future food justice in a resource-constrained world, Oxford: Oxfam GB for Oxfam International.

Portal, L. 2011.Commercial Pressures on Land [Online]. Available: http://landportal.info/topic/ commercial-pressures-land. Accessed 10/07/2012].

Temple, J. 1999. The new growth evidence. *Journal of economic literature,* 37, 112-156.

Williamson, O. E. 2000. The new institutional economics: taking stock, looking ahead. *Journal of economic literature,* 38, 595-613.

Chapter 9

Introduction of New Input Combination Package for Rice Production in Ebonyi State, Nigeria

[17]*Emmanuel Ogbodo,* [18]*Chukwuma Okereke,* [19]*Victor Chukwu and John Nwite*

9.1. Introduction

Rice is widely cultivated as a major crop in the tropical and sub- tropical regions of the African continent. In Nigeria, rice is not only important as food but serves as a source of raw material for agro-allied industries (Chinyelu,1999). Obiechina and Oti (1985) reported that in Nigeria, rice is the sixth major crop in the cultivable area after sorghum, millet, cowpea, cassava, and yam. It is the only crop in all agro-ecological zones from the Sahel to the coastal swamps. The Researchers further revealed that rice was widely regarded in Nigeria as superior food stuff, which until recently, was mainly consumed by city dwellers, the middle and higher income earners, and on occasions such as Christmas, marriages and naming ceremonies, by the peasants. Unfortunately, rice production in Nigeria has always fallen short of its demand in spite of huge investments in its productions. Also, in spite of the production resources in Nigeria, self-sufficiency in rice production and availability in the diet of average Nigerians are yet to be achieved (Agwangwa, 2004; Goni, et al., 2007).

---

[17]Department of Soil and Environmental Management, Ebonyi State University, Nigeria.

[18]Department of Agric Economics Management and Extention, Ebonyi State University, Nigeria.

[19] Ebonyi State Agricultural Development Programme, Nigeria

The major reasons for the decline in rice production was attributed to; insufficient use of resources, unfocused government policies, lack of agro-chemicals, lack of improved seeds, low soil fertility and high cost of labour among others (Goni, *et al.*, 2007; Okuneye, 2001; Akimbola 2002; Ohajianya and Onyejiaku 2002;. Awoke and Okorji, 2003). Agricultural production in Nigeria is labour intensive and more than 90 per cent of the rice producers are small-scale farmers cultivating one to two hectares, utilising unpaid family labour as a major source of farm labour supply (Olayide and Atobattele, 1980).

There is also a gap in knowledge between varieties of rice in the area resulting in low productivity. The combined effect of resources as explanatory variables in swamp rice production is still unknown to them. The rice farmers cultivate rice without reliable information on investment criteria and resource use efficiency. The farmers therefore need to be guided on what level of input combination that would ensure optimum profit. Spencer (2003) revealed that resource-poor farmers must be assisted to rise beyond subsistence to increase their incomes through more efficient use of resources.

According to Ali and Flinn (1989), opportunities for developing and adopting better technologies provide a possible solution for raising productivity and improve efficiency. Farmers in Nigeria need improved varieties of rice to increase yield. In Nigeria, Olagoke (1991) showed that irrigated rice farms had the highest yield of 2.19 tha^{-1} followed by swamp rice 1.96 tha^{-1} and then upland rice 1.17 tha^{-1}. However, NCRI (1988), reported that yields of 2.5-8.0 t ha^{-1} could be realised with high levels of fertiliser, improved varieties, optimum plant population, weed control and crop protection measures. The findings of this study would act as a guide to farmers on levels of input combination that would ensure optimum rice yield and profit.

9.2. Materials and Methods
9.2.1 Location
The study area covered the major rice growing areas across Ebonyi State. The state is situated within latitude 7^0 $30'$E and longitude 5^0 $40'$ N in Southeast Nigeria. The State has two distinct vegetation belts. The north and central portions have derived Guinea savannah while the south has forest belt. The soil is hydromophic, shallow in depth, with an impervious layer of parent material made of shale. The rainfall regime is bimodal, with peaks in July and September. The temperature ranges between 24^0 and 28^0. Annual rainfall ranges between 1500 mm and 2000 mm, while humidity averages 85 % during the rainy season. The soil is acidic, noted for high temperature, and high bulk density.

9.2.2 Experimental design
A multistage purposive and random sampling technique was employed in the study. For the purpose of selection of the experimental locations, the state was demarcated into three agricultural zones. Two local governments out of four per zone were chosen, giving a total of six local governments. Four major rice producing communities were selected per local government, giving a total of 24 farm communities. Ten rice farmers were randomly selected per community, giving a total of 240 participating farmers. Data for the analysis was generated from field survey involving the 240 farmers and researchers' field experiments using improved production package. All data obtained were scaled up to 1 ha as the standard unit of measurement for analytical purposes.

9.2.2.1 Treatments
The treatments comprised of a new input combination package and farmers local production practices. The new production package included improved rice varieties, herbicide and line planting, whereas the local production practices involved the landrace varieties and traditional cultural practices for rice production in the area.

9.2.2.2 Layout and treatment application

The agronomic study was conducted in the farmers' fields. The plots for the new package were laid besides the participating farmer's field in each experimental site. A land area of 0.5 ha each for the new varieties and the farmers plot respectively were used in each location. An alley, of 1 m wide was maintained between the two plots in each location. Glyphosate at the rate of 5 litres per hectare equivalent was used to kill the vegetation on the new package plots, two weeks before transplanting, while, the vegetation in the farmer's field was cleared manually with machetes.

The improved varieties were transplanted in rows, 20 cm apart and 20 cm between plants, while the landrace verities were transplanted in staggered method without consideration to planting space. The fertiliser component of the new package, equivalent of 100 kg of urea, and 200 kg of N P K 15: 15: 15 per hectare were applied to appropriate plots, while the farmers applied at varying rates of fertilisers, where available. For the improved package, half the rate of the urea was applied basally, 4 days before transplanting, while the remaining two thirds was applied alongside the N P K, by side placement, 4 weeks after transplanting.

The rice nurseries were made on beds established near the farms. The nurseries were established in May in the forest belt, and in June in the derived guinea savannah belt. The zero tillage method was used for the rice production. The grain yield was determined from a total of ten, 10 x 10 cm plots in each plot. The plots were randomly marked in each plot, the rice panicles harvested and heaped separately. The panicles were threshed, winnowed and the grains dried to 14 % moisture content. The mean weight of the grain harvests from each plot was calculated and the average for the ten plots converted to t ha[1].The data collected were analysed using descriptive and inferential statistics. Specifically, the analytical tools used include mean, coefficient of variation and t-test.

9.3. Results and Discussion
9.3.1 Costs and returns in rice production:

The costs and returns were evaluated to determine the profitability of rice production using the new production technology package and farmers' indigenous practices. The results obtained are presented in Tables 9.1, 9.2 and 9.3.

The result shows that total costs of production (TC) were ₦151, 400 and ₦153, 050 for the demonstration plots and farmers' plots respectively. These produced corresponding total revenues (TR) of ₦220, 000 and ₦188, 650 for the demonstration and farmers' plots respectively. Thus, the total revenue from the new package was higher than that from the farmers' indigenous system by ₦31, 350. The difference in the total revenues here is attributed to the difference in mean yields of the two production technology combinations which was 4.5 tha^{-1}. The test of the difference of two means using t-test also shows that this observed difference was statistically significant at the 1 % level of significance.

An assessment of the cost outlays shows that the inputs that contributed significantly to the total cost of production under the new production package were the agro-chemicals which had an aggregate value of ₦27, 100 representing 18% of the total cost. These include the cost of land clearing and weed control using chemical method. Similarly, labour for land clearing and weeding under the farmers' indigenous system amounted to ₦40, 000 representing 26% of the total cost of production. According to Akpokodje *et al.*, (2001), weed control constitutes the largest share of average total costs in rice production in Nigeria after land preparation.

Table 9.1: Costs of Production under Farmers Practice

Item	Unit	Quantity	Unit Price	Cost
Land	Ha	1	12,00	12,000
Seed	Kg	50	140.00	7,000
Clearing	Man days	20	800	16,000
Nursery Preparation	Person	1	1,200	1,200
Transplanting	Man days	32	800	25,600
Fertiliser	Bags	4	5,700	22,800
Fertiliser application	Man days	4	800	3,200
First weeding	Man days	20	800	16,000
Second weeding	Man days	10	800	8,000
Bird scaring	Persons	3	5000	15,000
Harvesting &threshing	20 persons	1ha	1,000	20,000
Bagging/bag stock	Tonnes	2.5	2,500	6,250
Total				153,050

Source: Field Survey Data (2009 and 2010 average)

Table 9.2: Costs of Production under the New Package

Item	Unit	Quantity	Unit Price	Cost
Land	Ha	1	12,000	12,000
Seed	Kg	50	140.00	7,000
Glyphosate	Litre	5	850	4000
Propanil	Litre	4	500	2000
2-4D	Litre	1	400	400
Spraying Glyphosate	Man days	7	800	5600
Nursery preparation	Persons	1	1,200	1,200
Transplanting	Man days	32	800	25,600
Urea	Bags	2	5,750	11,500
N P K	Bags	4	5,700	22,800
Applying N P K	Man days	4	800	3,200
Applying Urea	Man days	2	800	1,600
Spraying Propanil/24D	Ha	1	2000	2000
Bird Scaring	Persons	3	5,000	15,000
Harvesting/Threshing	20 Persons	1ha	1,000	20,000
Bagging/Bag stock	Tonne	7	2,500	17,500
Total				151,400

Source: Field Survey Data (2009 and 2010 average)

The respective net revenues (NR) from the new package and farmers' indigenous system were ₦68, 600 and ₦35, 600 showing a mean difference of ₦33, 000. The test of the difference between the means

139

shows that the net revenue from the demonstration plots was significantly higher than that of the farmers practice. This implies that rice production using the new production technology package was more profitable than that of the farmers' production system. Also, the average cost of production for the demonstration plot was ₦21, 536 t^{-1} while that of the farmers was ₦60, 494 t^{-1} showing a difference of N38, 958. This shows that there was more efficient utilisation of resources under the new input combination system than in the farmers' indigenous production system.

The average yields recorded in both the demonstration plots and the farmers' plots were significant improvement when compared to findings by Olagoke (1991), that the highest average rice yields per ha for irrigated, swamp and upland fields in Uzo-Uwani in the same Southeast Nigeria was 1.95 t ha^{-1}. This shows significant improvements in the land-area yield of rice due to technological improvements and the introduction of high-yielding rice varieties. This has translated into reduced average costs of production and enhanced revenue as well as increased levels of profitability. The adoption of agro-chemicals in weed control leads to reduced drudgery in rice production as well as increased profit margin. As such, there is a need to intensify efforts at getting the farmers in the study area to adopt fully the available improved input technology packages in their rice production towards greater productivity.

Table 9.3: Cost and Return on Rice Production

Variable	Demonstration Plot	Farmers' Plot
Cost	151,400	153,050
Gross income	220,000	188,650
Net income	68,600	35,600

Source: Field Survey Data (2009 and 2010 average)

9.3.2 Rice crop productivity

The results of the statistical analysis indicated that there was significantly higher rice grain yield when the new production package was applied, compared to the local production practices (Table 9.4). The grain yield of FARO 52 was 7.25 t ha^{-1}, representing 4.72 t ha^{-1} significantly higher grain yield (t-test at the 1 % level of significance) comparisons to grain yield of 2.53 t ha^{-1} of the farmers' best under the local production practices. The FARO 44 variety also had the yield of 6.44 t ha^{-1}, representing 3.91tha^{-1} significantly higher grain yield (t-test at the 1% level of significance) than the farmers' best under the local production practices. The average of the FARO varieties was 7.03 t ha^{-1} which showed 4.5 t ha^{-1} significantly higher grain yield (t-test at the 1 % level of significance) compared to the yield of the farmers' best. The variability in the yield of FARO 52 among the experiments was 55 %, which for FARO 44 was 42 %, whereas the variability in the yield of the farmers' varieties was 92 %.

This showed that the FARO varieties were more adaptable to vary between the soils of the area, particularly the inherent soil constraints of the study area. The soils of the area had been reported to suffer low soil fertility, resulting from its low organic matter content, low level of exchangeable bases and cation exchange capacity, buffer capacity and soil physical constraints including high bulk density, compaction and high soil temperature (Federal Department of Agricultural Land Resources, FDALR, 1985; Enwezor, *et al.*, 1990; Ogbodo, 2004; Ogbodo, 2005a; Ogbodo, 2005b).

There were no significant differences in grain yield among the two improved rice varieties under the improved production package. The implication of the comparable grain yield is that both varieties had comparable adaptability to the inherent poor soil conditions, and the improved soil productivity owing to the benefit of the new production package. Both had equal responses to the effect of an effective weed management, improved soil nutrient availability, and adequate feeding area. These situations culminated in enhanced crop productivity. The

141

application of herbicide brought about more efficient weed control. Weed interference constitutes a great problem to crop growth and yield, particularly during the critical periods of weed interference in crops life. The weeds compete with the target crops for space, soil nutrients, water, and sunlight. In some cases weeds increase incidences of pests, and disease attacks on crops.

Adequate fertiliser application improved the ability of the soil to provide necessary nutrients for increased plant growth and yield. Fertiliser application and management make a big difference in the yield of crops, particularly the improved varieties, which require heavier doses of fertiliser in order to fully express their genetic potentials. The higher dose of N-fertiliser and the management accounted in great measure for the outstanding difference in grain yield between the farmers' best under the local production practices and the improved varieties under the new production package.

The line planting technique ensured adequate plant population per unit land area, provided for the appropriate plant feeding area, and reduced competition for nutrients and water. These benefits ensured very vigorous and healthy plants, with less competition for sunlight, leading to improved plant photosynthetic efficiency. The combination of varietals disparity, poor production management, and weed interference, lower fertiliser application, restricted feeding area, and shading effect culminated in reduced crop productivity under the local production process.

Table 9.4: Rice Grain Yields

Variables	Yield (t ha⁻¹)	Variation Index	Coefficient of variation %
FARO 44	6.44	0.42	42
FARO 52	7.25	0.55	55
Landrace	2.53	0.36	36
Demonstration plot	7.03	0.76	76
Farmers' plot	2.53	0.92	92

Source: Field Survey Data (2009 and 2010 average)

9.4. Conclusion

The study demonstrated the disparity in grain yield and income from two rice production processes. The new production package improved rice grain yield compared to the local indigenous rice production practices. The two improved (FARO) varieties were more adaptable to the inherent soil conditions, with superior grain yield per ha compared to the farmers' landrace variety. The lower total production cost, higher grain yield and net revenue of the new production package, makes it more attractive. It was concluded that the new production package be adopted by the farmers in the state, as a means of increasing their rice grain yield output, and reducing the shortfall in rice production and supply in Nigeria.

References

Agwangwa, L. A. O. 2004. Imo joins crusade for self-sufficiency in rice". . National Agriculture Focus Magazine.

Akimbola, G. E. 2002. Poverty Reduction through the Crop Sub-Sector in Nigeria: A Regwnaz perspective Poverty Reduction and the Nigeria Agricultural Sector. El-Shadai: Global Ventures Limited.

Akpokodje, G., Frederic, L., Erenstein, O. and Bouake, C. 2001. The Nigerian rice economy in a competitive world: Constraints, opportunities and strategic choices. *West Africa Rice Development Association WARDA te dIvoire,* P15.

Ali, M. and Flinn, J. C. 1989. Profit Efficiency among Basmati Rice Producers in Punjab, Pakistan. . *American Journal of Agricultural Economics,* 1, 303-310.

Awoke, M. U. and Okorji, E. C. 2003. Analysis of constraints in resource use efficiency in multiple cropping systems by smallholder farmers in Ebony State of Nigeria. *Global Journal of Agricultural Sciences,* 2, 132-136.

Chinyelu, N. 1999. Rice processing and utilisation. *Special rice production Project Facilitating Training for Agricultural Officers from PTF and ADPs* Kaduna, Nigeria.

Enwezor, W. O., Ohiri, A. C., Opuwaribo, E. E. and Udo, E. 1990.A review of fertilizer use on crops in Southeastern zone of Nigeria. *Literature Review of Soil Fertility Investigations in Lagos, Nigeria.* Nigeria, : FMANR.

Federal Department of Agricultural Land Resources (FDALR) 1985. Reconnaissance Soil Survey of Anambra State, Nigeria. *Soils report.* Kaduna: FDALR.

Goni, M., Mohammed, S. and Baba, B. A. 2007. Analysis of resource-use efficiency in rice rroduction in Lake Chad Area of Bornu State, Nigeria. . *Journal of Sustainable Development in Agriculture,* 3, 31-37.

National Cereal Research Institute 1988. Hand Bulletin on Rice Production. Nigeria: National Cereal Research Institute, .

Obiechina, C. O. B. and Oti, F. 1985. Socio-economic impact of rice production technology on rural area of Anambra state, Nigeria. *Nigerian Journal of Rural Development,* 1, 132-147.

Ogbodo, E. N. 2004. Effect of tillage methods and crop residue mulch on soil physical conditions, growth and yield of irrigated maize at Abakaliki South-eastern. *Journal of the Science of Agriculture Food and Environment,* 4, 1-9.

Ogbodo, E. N. 2005a. Effect of depth of tillage on soil physical conditions, growth and yield of sweet potato in an Ultisol at Abakaliki South-eastern. *Journal of Agriculture and Social Research,* 5, 9-14.

Ogbodo, E. N. 2005b. Response of rice (Oryza sativa) to organic and inorganic manure in an Ultisol at Abakaliki South-eastern Nigeria. *Journal of Agriculture Forestry and Social Sciences,* 3, 9-14.

Ohajianya, D. O. and Onyejiaku, C. E. 2002. Farm size and relative efficiency in rice production in Ebony State, Nigeria. . *Modelling Simulation and Control Development Journal,* 3, 1-16.

Okuneye, P. A. 2001. Rising cost of food price and food insecurity in Nigeria and its implication for poverty reduction. *Central Bank of Nigeria Economic and Financial Review,* 39, 88-110.

Olagoke, M. A. 1991. Efficiency of Resource Use in Rice Production Systems in Anambra State, Nigeria.*In:* CHERYL, R. and DOSS AND CAROL OLSON (eds.) *African Rural Social Sciences Research Networks, Issues in African Rural Development.*

Olayide, S. O. and Atobattele, J. T. 1980. *Farm labours and Nigeria small farmers; Problems and prospects in integrated rural developments,* Ibadan, Nigeria, University of Ibadan Press

Spencer, D. 2003. The Future of Agriculture in Sub-Saharan Africa and Asia. Whither the small farm. International Conference 4-6 September, 2001 2002 Bonn, Germany 107-119

Chapter 10

Economic Impact of Climate Change on Value of Irrigated Rice Farms in Nigeria: A Ricardian Approach

[20]Ajetomobi Joshua Olusegun, [21]Ajiboye Abiodun, and [22]Rashid Hassan

10.1. Introduction

Like other developing countries, climate change is a potential threat to Nigerian agricultural and socioeconomic development. Generally, agricultural production activities have been found to be more vulnerable to climate change than other sectors (IPCC, 1990; Derresa et.al., 2005) and quite substantial works have been done in that respect at national, regional and global aggregate levels (Adams, 1989; Mendelsohn et.al., 1994; Munalula et.al., 1999; Chang 2002; Eid et. al., 2006; Nhemachena and Hassan, 2007; Molua and Lambi, 2007; Kurukulasuriya and Mendelsohn, 2007). Despite existing evidence that developing countries are more likely to be negatively affected by climate change than developed ones (IPCC, 1996), more efforts have been made to quantify the economic impacts of climate change on agriculture in developing countries than developed countries.

---

[20] Department of Agricultural Economics, Ladoke Akintola University of Technology, Nigeria

[21] Department of Agricultural Economics, Ladoke Akintola University of Technology, Nigeria

[22] Centre for Environmental Economics and Policy in Africa, University of Pretoria, South Africa

Even then, there has not been a major research carried out in Nigeria to study the economic impacts of climate change on agriculture. The vulnerability of the Nigerian agricultural sector to climate change could be of particular interest to policy makers because agriculture is a key sector in the economy. The sector accounts for between 60-70% of the labour force and constitutes between 30-40% of the nation's GDP. The sector is also the source of raw materials used in several processing industries as well as a source of foreign exchange earnings for the country. Though there seems to be an increase in food crop production generally in the nation, the country is not self- sufficient in the production of any food crop except cassava. The question remains therefore as to whether the production level will ever meet the demand level given the rate of population growth in the country.

Also, the proportion of change in production due to the impact of climate change will remain an important research focus as well as the measures needed to improve the resilience of the farmers to enable them adapt to climate change. A recent research has shown that rice can be used to offset the major impacts of climate change because of its potentials and unique properties as a food crop for urban poor and rural rice-growing populations (Manneh et. al., 2007).

Rice is a major cereal in Nigeria in terms of its output and land area. The crop is currently grown in more than 70% of the states in the country. In spite of the availability of cultivable land area, the current level of demand for rice in Nigeria is about 5 million metric tons which is more than twice the quantity produced (2.2 metric tons). At present about 4.9 million hectares are suitable for rice production but just about 1.8 (37%) are currently being utilised for cultivation. To amend the problem, West African Rice Development Agency (WARDA), International Institute for Tropical Agriculture (IITA) and the Ministry of Agriculture are frequently improving adaptation measures in rice agriculture in Nigeria.

In addition, Nigeria governments have invested more to increase rice production than other cereals. In 2009, the nation staked more than 10 billion Naira in public-private partnership schemes to improve the irrigation systems and set up about 17 new rice processing mills Bamba et.,al 2011).

The major problems associated with rice production include drought, flooding, salt stress and extreme temperatures, all of which are expected to worsen with climate change. Drastic changes in rainfall patterns and a rise in temperatures will introduce unfavourable growing conditions into the cropping calendars thereby modifying growing seasons which could subsequently reduce land value and hence the crop productivity. So far, there has not been any nationwide study in Nigeria that address the economic impacts of climate change in value of land for rice farming and farm level adaptations that rice farmers make to mitigate the potential impact of such climate change.

The main objective of this study therefore is to analyse the economic impact of climate change in the value of land for rice production in Nigeria. Specifically, the study (i) estimated a traditional Ricardian model using land rent as the dependent variable unlike previous works which used net revenue and (ii) evaluated the importance of irrigation as an alternative course of action to mitigate the likely impact of climate change on the value of land for rice farming in Nigeria.

The distinction between irrigated and non-irrigated rice cultivation is very relevant in Nigeria since irrigation is necessitated by prolong drought effects. As at 2005, irrigated rice production accounted for up to 20% of the total rice area in the country. Other inputs normally altered in rice agriculture include the use of fertiliser, insecticide and herbicide. Varying amounts of nitrogenous fertiliser is required to take full advantage of carbon dioxide effects or decrease to minimise input costs. The timing of application can also be altered depending on the pattern of precipitation. This paper is organised as follows: section one is the introduction, section two discusses the Ricardian approach adopted including specification of the empirical model and estimation procedures. The results and discussion are presented in section three while section four gives the summary and conclusion.

149

10.2. Materials and Methods

The econometric approach used in this study is based on the Ricardian method to assess economic impacts of climatic changes, which allows for capturing adaptations farmers make in response to climate changes. The method was named after David Ricardo (1772 – 1823) because of his original observation that land value would reflect its net productivity. The principle is shown explicitly in the following equation:

$$LV = \sum P_i Q_i(X,F,H,Z,G) - \sum P_x X \dots \dots \dots (1)$$

Where LV is the value of land, Pi is the market price of the crop i, Q_i is the quantity of crop i produced, X is a vector of purchased inputs (except land), F is a vector of climate variables, H is water flow, Z is a vector of soil variables, G is a vector of socioeconomic variables and Px is a vector of input prices (Mendelsohn et.al, 1994). It is assumed that the farmer chose X so as to maximise land value per hectare given characteristics of the farm and market prices. The dependent variable therefore is the capitalised net revenues (land values).Following Mendelsohn et. al (2007), the standard Ricardian model relies on a quadratic formulation of climate:

$$LV/ha = \beta_0 + \beta_1 F + \beta_2 F^2 + \beta_3 Z + \beta_4 G + \mu \dots \dots (2)$$

Where LV/ha is land value measured by rent per hectare respectively, F is the vector of climate variables, Z is a set of soil variables, G is a set of socioeconomic characteristics, μ is the error term. Both linear and quadratic terms for temperature and precipitation are introduced.

In this study, land rent as a measure of the value of agricultural land was available for 491 (About 41%) out of 1200 respondents. Out of the 491 farmers, about 48% of them irrigated their farms. Since the complete data set comprises a survey of 1200 rice farms from 20 states in Nigeria, the analysis of the data at this stage was truncated. This is because the dependent variable – land rent per hectare - was not observed in 709 out of 1200 farmers. The usual approach for dealing with this kind of incidental truncation is to include an explicit equation for the population of interest. Generally, sample selection is only problematic from an econometric point of view if the error term of the sample selection equation is correlated with the error term from the equations of primary interest. Heckman's method for correcting this source of bias was used in this study. This involves identifying variables that could be included in the selection equation but which do not appear as independent variables in the primary equation (Heckman, 1979).

STATA 10.0 software was used to fit the Heckman sample selection bias models. To overcome the problems of heteroscedasticity and multicollinearity, a robust estimation of the standard error was undertaken and identified correlated variables were dropped from the models. Variables were dropped from the model on the basis of low significance level and low contribution in improving the overall significance of the estimated models. The expected marginal impact of single climate variability on the land value was evaluated at the mean as follows:

$$E[dLV / df_i] = b_{1,i} + 2 * b_{2,i} * E[f_i] \dots\dots\dots\dots\dots\dots\dots\dots \quad (3)$$

The signs of the linear terms indicate the uni-directional impact of the independent variables on the dependent variable, the quadratic term reflects the non-linear shape of the climate response function. When the quadratic term is positive, the land rent function is U shaped and when the quadratic term is negative the function is hill-shaped. Agronomic studies showed that crops consistently exhibit a hill-shaped relationship with annual temperature, although the maximum of that hill varies with the crop.

The advantage of this empirical approach is that the method includes both direct effect of climate on productivity and the adaptation response by farmers to local climate. An observed drawback of the Ricardian approach however has been its explicit exclusion of irrigation. Cline (1996) and Darwin (1999) both argue in favour of inclusion of irrigation in the analysis. Several researchers (Mendelsohn et al, 1994); Mendelsohn and Dinar, 2003; Schlender et.al, 2005) had attempted to address the problem by modelling irrigation. Following Kurukulasuriya and Mendelsohn (2008), this study explicitly examined dry land and irrigated land as well as water flow as a measure of hydrology. The Ricardian analysis in this study clearly does take cognisance of irrigation.

10.2.1 Data and empirical analysis

Farm-level data on land rent and its determinants were collected from 1200 randomly selected rice farmers spread all over the agro-ecological zones. The survey covered 20 states in the country, which were selected to represent the major rice producing regions in the country, namely, Kano, Niger, Benue, Yobe, Kaduna, Anambra, Ebonyi, Kwara, Edo, Taraba and Kebbi states, Zamfara, Jigawa, Borno, Adamawa, Ondo, Ogun, Cross River, Ekiti, and Kogi states. There were significant variations in temperatures and precipitations of the states. The differences are driven by elevations.

A sample of 60 rice farmers was randomly selected from each state, making a total of 1200 respondents. The data were collected with the use of a structured questionnaire administered to the rice farmers between September 2008 and January 2009. The questionnaire came from Yale University and the University of Pretoria. The questionnaire had two main parts and six sections. Part 1 focused on crop production and Part 2 on livestock. Sections 1 and 2 asked about household characteristics and the household head's employment. The questions in Section 3 were about the household's land under farming activities (both crops and livestock), and about the labour used for various farm activities and their costs.

In Section 4 detailed questions are asked about crop farming activities: the type of crops grown, the area of land planted, and the quantities of crops harvested and sold, and various costs such as seeds, fertiliser and pesticides; light, heavy and light and heavy machinery and animals used in agricultural work; and farming related buildings. Section 4 asked about the types of animals farmed and how many were purchased, lost and sold during the growing season, and about livestock and poultry products, such as milk, beef, wool and eggs. Section 5 asked about the farmers'

access to information on farming activities and the sources and the cost
of this information, and Section 6 asked for an estimate of the farm
household's total income (for both farming and non-farming activities),
taxes paid and subsidies received. Finally, Section 7 contained questions
on farmers' perceptions of short- and long-term climate change and their
adaptation strategies in response to these.

According to Erenstein et. al (2003), rice farmers in Nigeria engaged in
other farming and off-farm activities. Such other farm activities include
growing of other cereals, tuber and tree crops as well as animal
husbandry. Examples of their off-farm activities were fishing, hunting,
salaried work, commerce, transport and other vocational jobs.

January to December monthly means for precipitation and temperature
from 1970 to 2007 were specifically obtained from the Nigeria
Meteorological Agency at Oshodi in Lagos Nigeria and International
Institute for Tropical Agriculture (IITA) in Ibadan, Nigeria. During the
survey period, there were 32 stations in the country. Given significant
variation in temperatures across geographic locations (driven primarily
by elevation) the study accounted for seasonal temperatures and
precipitations.

The soil data for the 20 states producing rice in Nigeria were obtained
from the Food and Agricultural Organisation (FAO). The FAO provides
information about the major and minor soils in each location, including
the slope and texture. In all, there existed 5 types of soil in the states
during the survey period and all of them were used in the analysis. The
distribution of the soil by the states is shown in Table 10.1. Runoffs data
for various regions in the country were obtained from Global Centre for
Hydrological Data in Germany. Runoff is defined as excess precipitation,
which is not absorbed by soils. It runs on the soil surface and eventually
joins a stream. Runoff takes away soil nutrients. Excessive runoff may
have a negative impact on farm yield. It is abundantly clear from the
literature that irrigation and water availability are important to rice
production in Nigeria. Irrigated lands are generally of higher value when

compared to farms that rely solely on rain. Farms that rely only on rainwater were classified as dry land. Those that relied at least on surface water resources, groundwater or stored water in any season of the survey year were assumed to be irrigated.

Table 10. 1: State soil Variable

State	Soil type
Kano	(Gb)- Brown and Reddish Brown soil of Arid and Semi-arid Regions (not differentiated)
Niger	(Jc)- Ferruginous Tropical Soils on Crystalline Acid Rocks
Benue	(Ln)- Ferrallite Soils, Dominant Colour Red (not differentiated)
Yobe	(Gb)- Brown and Reddish Brown soil of Arid and Semi-arid Regions (not differentiated)
Kaduna	(Jc)- Ferruginous Tropical Soils on Crystalline Acid Rocks
Anambra	(Li)- Ferrallite Soils, Dominant Colour Red on Loose Sandy Sediments.
Ebonyi	(Ln)- Ferrallite Soils, Dominant Colour Red
Kwara	(Jc)- Ferruginous Tropical Soils on Crystalline Acid Rocks
Edo	(La)- Ferrallitic Soils, Dominant Colour Yellowish – Brown,
Taraba	(Jc)- Ferruginous Tropical Soils on Crystalline Acid Rocks
Kebbi	(Jc)- Ferruginous Tropical Soils on Crystalline Acid Rocks
Ekiti	(Jc)- Ferruginous Tropical Soils on Crystalline Acid Rocks
Kogi	(Jc)- Ferruginous Tropical Soils on Crystalline Acid Rocks
Zamfara	(Jc)- Ferruginous Tropical Soils on Crystalline Acid Rocks
Jigawa	(Gb)- Brown and Reddish Brown soil of Arid and Semi-arid Regions (not differentiated)
Borno	(Gb)- Brown and Reddish Brown soil of Arid and Semi-arid Regions (not differentiated)
Adamawa	(Jc)- Ferruginous Tropical Soils on Crystalline Acid Rocks
Ondo	(Jc)- Ferruginous Tropical Soils on Crystalline Acid Rocks
Ogun	(Li)- Ferrallite Soils, Dominant Colour Red on Loose Sandy Sediments.
Cross River	(La)- Ferrallitic Soils, Dominant Colour Yellowish – Brown, (not differentiated)

Source: FAOSTAT Database

In addition to the climate and soil variables, we collected information about the farmer characteristics. These include the household head's education level to capture effects such as the ability of households to adopt new technologies, as well as ability to better optimise on farming and marketing practices. The survey also obtained information about the farmer's experience, which is expected to have a positive impact on farm profitability. The socio-economic data obtained from the survey also include the gender of the household head, household size, farm size, educational status, access to public extension services, access to credit, amount of crop consumed, amount of crop sold by type of markets, the use of machinery, the cost of labour used, the values in kilometres of distance to market from where inputs were purchased and output sold.

The response variable for the study was per hectare land value for rice farming measured in terms of rent paid by the farmers. The dependent variable was regressed on climate and other important control variables, such as soils and socioeconomic data. After estimating the models above, simulations were undertaken using different climate scenarios to determine how value of land for rice production will be affected under the scenario.

10.3. Results and Discussion

10.3.1 Descriptive statistics

Table 10. 2: Descriptive Statistics of Variables for the Ricardian model

Variable	All farms		Irrigated farms		Dry land farms	
	Mean	Std. Dev.	Mean	Std. Dev.	Mean	Std. Dev.
Land rent per hectare	2682.05	2879.08	2824.98	2923.16	2585.76	2847.00
January rain	5.95	7.04	1.11	2.16	9.22	7.30
April rain	90.80	64.41	44.68	32.12	121.86	62.06
July rain	223.91	71.36	194.06	29.58	244.02	83.25
October rain	123.95	95.60	56.19	42.93	169.60	94.23
January temperature	32.86	1.75	32.51	2.07	33.10	1.44
April temperature	36.14	2.86	37.98	2.05	34.90	2.65
July temperature	30.24	1.68	31.05	1.47	29.69	1.59
October temperature	32.51	1.98	33.54	1.69	31.82	1.85
Squared January rain	84.93	161.02	5.88	17.16	138.18	190.16
Squared April rain	12388.84	13557.17	3026.17	3888.29	18695.91	14093.86
Squared July rain	55222.32	40474.30	38530.87	11263.18	66466.36	48407.65
Squared October rain	24495.51	30591.43	4996.63	6321.16	37630.74	33331.34
Squared January temperature	1082.78	113.29	1060.96	133.90	1097.48	94.27
Squared April temperature	1314.27	207.54	1446.58	153.58	1225.14	191.01
Squared July	917.17	103.51	966.30	91.55	884.08	97.86

temperature						
Squared	1060.89	130.94	1127.86	114.15	1015.78	121.96
October temperature						
Gb soil	0.10	0.30	0.17	0.37	0.06	0.23
Jc soil	0.49	0.50	0.55	0.50	0.44	0.50
Ln soil	0.10	0.30	0.03	0.16	0.15	0.36
Li soil	0.10	0.30	0.12	0.33	0.08	0.28
La soil	0.15	0.36	0.00	0.00	0.25	0.43
Mean flow	1884.22	1647.58	1296.37	755.82	2280.22	1941.90
Farm area	3.76	2.37	3.56	2.24	3.90	2.44
Credit	0.43	0.59	0.59	0.57	0.32	0.57
Irrigated	0.40	0.49	1.00	0.00	0.00	0.00

Source: Compiled by Author

The basic summary statistics of the dataset for the relevant variables of the study are presented in Table 10.2. The mean value of land rent per hectare for irrigated rice farms was greater than that of dry land rice farms. The values were N2879.08 and 2685.76 respectively. This paper considered two climate data namely temperature and precipitation and their mean values in January, April, July and October. The mean rainfall and temperature variations across the two categories of farms were considered in this study. As expected, irrigated rice farm regions were generally warmer than dry land rice farms in all the months due to lower level of precipitation.

The soil type on which the farmers operated is a function of geographical location. These soil types were (Gb)- Brown and Reddish Brown soil of Arid and Semiarid Regions (not differentiated); (Jc)- Ferruginous Tropical Soils on Crystalline Acid Rocks; (Li)- Ferrallite Soils, Dominant Colour Red on Loose Sandy Sediments.; (Ln)- Ferrallite Soils, Dominant Colour Red (not differentiated); (La)- Ferrallitic Soils, Dominant Colour Yellowish – Brown,(not differentiated). More than half of the irrigated rice farmers (55%) planted in Jc soil type. The same set of farmers that used Gb, Li, Ln and La were in the proportion of 17%, 12%, 3%,and 0% respectively. On the other hand, about 44% of dry land rice farmers plant on Jc soil while 6%, 8%, 15% and 25% used

157

Gb, Li, Ln, and La respectively. The dominant soil types in various states are shown in Table 10.1.

The average total area devoted to rice cultivation was 3.76 hectares. This suggests that rice farming in Nigeria is still predominantly on small scale level. More land area on the average was devoted to dry land rice farming (3.90) than irrigated (3.56). Access to credit also varied widely across the two categories of rice growers. On the average, about 59 % of the irrigated rice farmers had access to formal credit, whereas less than one third (32 %) of dry land rice farmers had access. The sales of produce to urban market followed the same pattern, about 61% of irrigated rice farmers sold their rice at urban market while the proportion was about 54 % of dry land rice farmers. Accessibility to land depends mostly on whether a farmer is a native of a particular location or not.

There were four main modes of land acquisition identified by the farmers. About 41 % of the farmers rented their crop land, while 59% got their land through other means such as leasing and communal land tenure system. In order to reduce the side effects of unfavourable climatic conditions, about 65% and 57% of the irrigated rice farmers and dry land rice farmers respectively engaged in various off-farm works. These include civil service, artisan, teaching and other vocational activities. The average distance of the market place to the farm was about 49km for irrigated rice farmers and 57.12km for dry land rice farmers.

The summary of the personal characteristics shows that on the average, irrigated rice farmers were more educated than dry land rice farmers. The average gaming experience however did not follow that pattern. Their average farming experience was 16.54 and 19.02 for irrigated rice farmers and dry land rice farmers respectively. The average number of extension visits also differs by categories of rice farms. Quite interesting, the extension agents visited dry land rice farmers than irrigated rice farmers perhaps because they were less educated and therefore required more attention. In respect of livestock farming, it was far more prevalent among dry land rice farmers (71%) than irrigated rice farmers (28%) as a climate adaptation option.

10.3.2 The regression results

The analysis explored three principal hypotheses: first, land value per hectare is sensitive to climate. Second, irrigated and dry land rice farms have different response to climate (Mendelsohn and Dinar 2003, Schlenker et al. 2005). Third, land rent per hectare has different climate response functions. These hypotheses were tested by estimating the following regressions (i) the land rent per hectare for all the farms (ii) the land rent per hectare of irrigated rice and (iii) the land rent per hectare for dry land rice. Land rent per hectare was the response variable. It was regressed on climate and other control variables (Table 3). A non-linear (quadratic) model was chosen for ease of interpretation.

In the initial runs, the independent variables include both the linear and quadratic temperature and precipitation term. Three definitions of the climate variables were tried; firstly, they were defined in terms of four seasons: Winter (average for December, January and February), Spring (the average for March, April and May), Summer (the average for June, July and August) and Fall in (September, October and November). Secondly, they were defined in terms of the predominant seasons in the country which are rainy (April to October) and dry (November to March) seasons. Thirdly, they were defined as the middle months for Winter, Spring, Summer and Fall, that is, January, April, July, and October. The results for the third definition had the best statistical quality. Hence it is reported and discussed in this paper.

10.3.3 Land rent regression models

The regression results for the Heckman sample selection model are shown in Table 3. The variables used to identify the model included among others, whether the respondent worked off farm, family size, education of the respondents in the year, whether the respondent sells at urban market and the farming experience of the respondents. The results of the modelling in Table 10.3 showed that more climate variables were more significant in dry land rice farms than in irrigated rice farms. Apart from October temperature which was positive, and significantly related to land rent for irrigated rice farms, other temperature variables were insignificant. They were however significant for dry land rice farm model. The second order temperature had a positive and significant effect on land rent for irrigated rice farms. On the contrary, a U-shaped relationship was observed for precipitation in January and April for dry land rice farms.

Table 10.3: Heckman Sample Selection Model: Dependent Variable = Land Rent/ha

Variable	All Farms		Irrigated		Dry	
	Coefficient	t-value	coefficient	t-value	Coefficient	t-value
Constant	1340408	2.65	-209956.3	-1.5	610946.5	1.33
January rain	-660.86	-1.16			-5272.48	-2.2
April rain	139.33	1.66	1179.09	1.56	-1019.09	-1.96
July rain	42.58	0.79	-468.13	-1.56	600.44	1.87
October rain	-86.72	-0.98	1555.59	1.67	846.41	2.37
January temperature	-57291.43	-2.84				
April temperature	19765.51	1.66			-32572.93	-1.32
July temperature						
October temperature	-45693.86	-2.39				
Squared January rain	19.82	0.77	208.87	1.28	238.94	2.12
Squared April rain	-0.47	-1.64	-4.33	-1.45	3.05	2.18
Squared July rain	-0.1	-0.8	1.66	1.65	-1.51	-1.96
Squared October rain	2775663	1.32	-8.86	-1.71	-1.56	-2.56
Squared January temperature	871.6	2.82	-107.46	-1.63	7.48	0.35
Squared April temperature	-286.66	-1.8	-40.52	-2.98	409.17	1.33
Squared July temperature	-27.24	-1.16	-156.05	-1.57	46.14	1.07
Squared October temperature	731.15	2.52	429.33	1.69	-62.86	-1.23
Gb soil	-10186.14	-2.43			11100.29	1.42
Jc soil	-1274.03	-1.43	-615.44	-0.64	-2624.4	-1.37
Ln soil	-3688.11	-2.03			229.72	0.12
Li soil	-3160.79	-2.02			9030.25	1.81
La soil						
Mean flow	-0.62	-3.05	-1.39	-1.89	-2.46	-1.46
Farm area	26.55	0.59	-1.12	-0.02	26.87	0.46
Credit	-369.77	-1.69	-98.58	-0.34	-488.46	-1.47
Irrigated	554.74	1.92				

Source: Compiled by Author

The results showing the relevance of various soil types showed that none of them was significant for both irrigated and dry land rice model. The run-off variable was however negatively and significantly related to land rent per hectare for all rice farms and irrigated rice farms. This showed

that the implicit value of land is lower in areas characterised by high level
of runoff.

Turning to the selection equation (Table 10.4), educational status of the
respondents, farming experience in years and market distance
significantly affected land rent for irrigated rice farms. Apart from
market distance, the variables were positive. Surprisingly, none of the
variables significantly affected land rent for dry land rice farms. The
Wald test however, readily rejects the hypothesis that the regression
equation and the selection equation are independent of one another,
justifying the use of the Heckman model.

Table 10. 4: Heckman Sample Selection Model: Selection equation

Variable	All farms		Irrigated farms		Dry land farms	
	coefficient	T	coefficient	t	coefficient	T
Constant	0.41	2.59	0.3	1.31	0.58	2.71
Mean flow	0	0.33				
Farm area	-0.02	-0.96	-0.01	-0.51	-0.02	-1.03
Credit	0.03	0.37	0.1	0.85	-0.08	-0.84
Irrigated	0.04	0.51				
Urban market	0.01	0.16	0.18	1.45	-0.11	-1.12
Non-farm job	-0.06	-0.73	-0.12	-0.98	-0.03	-0.32
Market distance	0	0.58	0.01	2.4	0	-1.11
Rice farming experience	-0.01	-2.67	-0.01	-2.61	-0.01	-1.53
Family size	0	0.3	-0.01	-0.82	0.01	1.05
Extension contact	0.03	1.35	0.03	1.47	0.02	0.77
Livestock keeping	0.01	0.2	0.13	1.07	-0.01	-0.2
Educational status	-0.01	-1.57	-0.02	-1.94	0	-0.45
N	1200		483		717	
Censored observation	491		191		300	
Wald chi2	140.65		94.03		64.46	

Source: Compiled by Author

10.3.4 Marginal impact analysis of land rent model

The marginal impact analysis was also conducted to assess the effect of an infinitesimal change in temperature and precipitation on land rent per hectare. Dry land rice land rent fell at an average of N4778.31 per 1°C rise in temperature (Table 10.5). On the contrary, land rent per hectare for irrigated rice farms increase with increase in temperature. A breakdown of the results of various months showed that April and October temperatures were harmful to land rent per hectare for dry land rice farming while October temperature was particularly beneficial to irrigated farms. The marginal effects of precipitation on land rent per hectare also varied across farm types. For instance, increasing precipitation on irrigated rice farms by 1 mm would increase land rents by 1991.91 per annum but reduced it by 1035.48 for dry land farms.

Table 10. 5: Marginal Effect of temperature and precipitation on land rent per hectare

Temperature	January	April	July	October	Annual
All farms	-9.88	-954.28	-1647.48	1845.51	-766.12
Irrigated	-6987.05	-3077.9	-9690.71	28799.46	9043.80
Dry	495.18	-4012.86	2739.79	-4000.41	-4778.31

Precipitation	January	April	July	October	Annual
All farms	-425	53.98	-2.20	-17.31	-390.53
Irrigated	1642.78	-855.06	2199.87	-995.69	1991.91
Dry	-940.19	-275.74	-136.5	316.95	-1035.48

Source: Compiled by Author

10.3.5 Impacts of forecasted climate scenario on rice land rent

The simulation results for land rent models are shown in Table 10.6.
Increasing precipitation will decrease the value of land for both irrigated
and dry land farm. In similar fashion, simultaneously changing both
temperatures (+2°C) and precipitation (-5%) will have a harmful effect
on land rent for both irrigated and dry land rice farming.

Table 10. 6: Impact of changing only temperature or rainfall on rice land rent in percentage %

Climate Variable	Climate Scenarios	All farm	Irrigated	Dry
Temperature	+2 °C	0.00	8.79	-10.46
Rainfall	-5%	95	-9.6	-13.15
Both temperature and rainfall	+2°C and 5% reduction in rainfall	-9	-34.69	-19.84

Source: Compiled by Author

10.4. Conclusion and Implication

The empirical results from this study provide certain evidence that
climate change is significant to rice production in Nigeria. The results
showed that land rent per hectare was sensitive to marginal change in
climate variables (temperature and precipitation). The degree of
sensitivity however depends on whether the farm is irrigated or not.
Generally, the value of land used for rice production was more sensitive
to marginal changes in temperature than precipitation. The results have
some implications for the relevance of irrigation as an adaptation
technique.

- The results suggest that the use of irrigation has proved to be an
  effective adaptation measure to reduce the harmful effects of
  climate change on rice agriculture. However, most river basins in

the country are under-performing. They are ineffective in meeting the demand of rice farmers in Nigeria. Further investments are therefore required to resuscitate the irrigation systems both in terms of facilities and manpower.

- Since land rent was sensitive to marginal changes in climate variables, efforts should be geared towards having a well-functioning land market in the nation. The on-going review of the nation's land use and reforms for instance should be given this utmost consideration.

- By and large, given the increasing investment by the Nigeria government to increase rice production, wider research and deeper analyses of climate change on its agriculture should be encouraged.

Acknowledgment

The authors gratefully acknowledge the financial and technical contributions to the research by the Centre for Environmental Economics and Policy in Africa (CEEPA), South Africa. However, the views expressed in this report, as well as any errors, are entirely attributable to the authors.

References

Adams, R. M. 1989. Global climate change and agriculture: An economic perspective. *American Journal of Agricultural Economics,* 71, 1272-1279.

Akpokodje, G. A., Lancon, F. and Olaf, E. 2002. Nigeria's Rice Policy and Development: A Review. *Final Draft.* Abidjan, Cote d' Ivoire: WARDA.

Bamba, I and J. Manful and O. Ajayi 2011. Historic Opportunity for Rice Growers in Nigeria Revue Grain de sel 51 : Special Issue

Chang, C. 2002. The potential impact of climate change on Taiwan's agriculture. *Agricultural Economics,* 27 51-64.

Cline, W. 1996. The Impact of Climate Change on Agriculture: Comment. *American Economic Review,* 86, 1309-1311.

Darwin, R., Tsigas, M., Lewabdrowski, J. and Raneses, A. 1995. World Agriculture and Climate Change. *Agricultural Economic Report No. 703*

(June). Washington, DC:: US Department of Agricultural, Economic Research Service.

Deressa, T., R., H. and Poonyth, D. 2005. Measuring The Impact of Climate Change on South African Agriculture: The Case of Sugar Cane Growing Regions. *Agrekon* 44 SRC – Google Scholar.

Eid, H. M., Marsafawy, S. M. and Oudai, S. A. 2006. Assessing the economic impacts of climate change on agriculture in Egypt a Ricardian approach Research. *Journal of Agriculture and Biological Sciences,* 2, 316-322.

Erenstein, O. 2003. Smallholder conservation farming in the tropics and sub-tropics, A guide to the dissemination of mulching with crop residues. *Agriculture, Ecosystem and Environment,* 21, 17-37.

F. A. O. 2004. *Nigeria: Annual Report on Rice Production and Consumption* [Online]. FAOSTAT database. Available: http://ww.fao.org/es/ess/top/country.Jsp.

Heckman J. J. 1979 Sample Selection Bias as a Specification Error. Econometrica 47 (1) : 156-161

IPCC (Intergovernmental Panel on Climate Change) 1990. *Scientific assessment of climate change,* New York, World Metrological Organisation and United Nations Environmental Program.

IPCC (Intergovernmental Panel on Climate Change) 1996. *Impacts, adaptations and mitigation of climate change: Scientific-technical analyses,* Cambridge, UK, Cambridge University Press.

Kurukulasuriya, P. and Mendelsohn, R. 2007. Endogenous irrigation: The impact of climate change on farmers in Africa. *World Policy Research Working Paper 4278.*

Kurukulasuriya, P., Mendelsohn, R. and A. 2008. A Ricardian analysis of the impact of climate change on African cropland. *AfJARE* 2, 1-23.

Manneh, B., Kiepe, P., Sie, M., Ndjiondjop, M., Drame, N. K., Traore, K., Rodenburg, J., Somado, E. A., Narteh, L., Youm, O., Diagne, A. and Futakuchi, K. 2007. Exploiting Partnerships in Research and Development to help African Rice Farmers cope with Climate Variability" Paper presented at *ICRISAT and CGIAR 35th Anniversary Symposium "Climate-Proofing Innovation for Poverty Reduction and Food Security.*

Mendelsohn, R. 2007. Measuring climate impacts with cross sectional analysis. *Climate Change,* 18 1-7.

Mendelsohn, R. and Dinar, A. 2003. Climate, water, and agriculture. *Land Economics*, 79, 328-341.

Mendelsohn, R., Nordhaus, W. D. and Shaw, D. 1994. The impact of global warming on agriculture: analysis. *American Economic Review*, 84 753-771.

Molua, E. L. and Lambi, C. M. 2007. The economic impact of climate change on agriculture in Cameroon. *The World Bank Policy Research Working Paper 4364.*

Munalula, T., Nkomoki, J., Nawiko, M. and Kamocha, S. 1999. Estimating the impact of climate change on rain-fed agriculture: A cross-sectional analysis of impacts on medium and small scale agricultural revenue in Zambia. Lusaka, Zambia: Ministry of Environment and Natural Resources

Nhemachema, C. and Hassan, R. 2007. Micro-Level Analysis of farmers' adaptation to climate change in South Africa. *IFFRI discussion paper 00714.*

Schlenker, W., Hanemann, W. M. and Fisher, A. C. 2005. Will US Agriculture Really benefits from global warning? Accounting for irrigation in Hedonic approach. . *American Economic Review*, 95, 395-406.

Chapter 11

Land and Water Resources for Improved Food Security and Ecosystem Service in Africa: Looking Ahead

[23]*Elias T. Ayuk, Effiom E. Oku and Kwabena O. Asubonteng*

Food is a basic necessity for survival. It is therefore imperative for every country to ensure that her citizenry have access to adequate food. However this is usually not the case in Sub -Saharan African (SSA) countries. Most of these countries are blessed with abundant land and water resources, yet are bedevilled with food insecurity challenges. In contrast, Japan and other countries, poor in natural resources have been able to blossom economically and ensure food security for their population mainly backed by science and technology.

Africa must therefore invest in innovative science and technology research with the view of enhancing the management of natural resources for sustainable development. Science and technology are the obvious means for changing the trajectories for harnessing Africa's land and water resources to create wealth, produce enough food and reduce poverty. In Africa, there is a huge human capital deficit in research and science.

According to UNU-INRA (2011), there are only 70 researchers per one million people in Africa, compared with 130 in the Middle East and India, 550 in Latin America, 1990 in Europe, 2,640 in North America

---

[23] United Nations University Institute for Natural Resources in Africa (UNU-INRA

and 4,380 in Japan. This gap necessitates the building of scientific capacities with continuous upgrading of teaching and research facilities in science and technology in Africa. This will produce a pool of "science-based" researchers who are important for providing solutions for natural resources management for the continent. Land, an important natural resource is one of the most mismanaged resources in SSA.

Land management institutions in many SSA countries are said to be weak and therefore have allowed large land acquisitions or 'land grabs' by foreign multinationals and even local elites. This phenomenon has made Africa a hotspot for large land acquisitions by foreign companies, especially in the last seven years when financial, food and energy crises hit the World. Many of the hectares of land acquired were said to be used for biofuel and agrofuel crop plantations.

This has serious consequences for food and water security due to the degradation occasioned by the insatiable demand for land for cultivation and water for irrigation. The land acquisition is further implicated in creating land disputes leading to food and nutritional insecurity, and biodiversity loss. The consequences are obviously loss of livelihoods for about 80 million smallholder farmers and pastoralists. With the quest for a carbon free economy, the quest for biofuel crops will continue though Africa is yet to benefit from the huge share of the global fund that accrues from this source.

Despite the challenges reportedly posed by biofuel production in Africa, there are arguments in its favour. According to UNIDO (2009), biofuel production on the continent will reduce the dependence on imported fuels thereby saving the meagre foreign exchange needed in other pressing sectors of the economy. The report indicates that currently, 39 countries in Africa are net oil importers. The report cites Brazil as a country that substitutes its oil import with ethanol to the tune of $60.7 billion. It is argued that the use of rural lands for biofuel production will improve rural economies, increase access to reliable green energy supply and create employment. As a first step, the development of biofuels in SSA should initially focus on ensuring energy access for the local markets

and only turn to international markets once local capacities and
sustainability standards are in place.

There is also an argument that biofuel production is necessary for future
energy security in Africa given the increasing population growth and the
threats of climate change. But biofuel production should not compete
with food crop production in terms of land use. Lal (2008), estimates
that about 62 million ha of Africa's land is chemically degraded. Fifteen
million ha of the degraded lands was   by means of salinization. This
large area can rightly be classified as a wasteland and thus could be
harnessed for meeting Africa's green energy needs.

Green fuel, will in the foreseeable future, play a vital role in economies
worldwide. Jatropha, the popular green fuel plant grows very well on
saline soils. India's experience of converting its wasteland to Jatropha
plantation can be replicated in Africa, converting these large hectares of
wasteland to Jatropha fields for green fuel production is a possibility
mainly because the plant tolerates drought. Grag et al., (2011) report that
converting wasteland to Jatopha production as done in India creates a
win-win situation. They argue that the use of wasteland for Jatropha
production will help improve soil carbon and land productivity. It will
create supplementary source of income, contribute to climate change
mitigation through carbon sequestration and help in the production of
green energy and feedstock.

The challenges discussed in previous chapters in this book are that,
institutions responsible for land negotiations and the enforcement of rule
of law when it comes to foreign land transactions in most African
countries are weak. In order to maximise Africa's natural resources for
the benefit of all, there is the need for African countries to foster greater
regional integration and build strong institutions which could formulate
and implement robust laws. SSA countries should equally eschew
corruption so that land deals are transparent to local people who might
be affected by such transactions. Coherent and consistent policy and

regulatory frameworks are central to the successful harnessing of renewable energy in Africa.

It is not in doubt that such frameworks are absent in many SSA countries and where they exist they are weak in content and implementation. Many central governments in Africa lack a clear direction and leadership in matters relating to land dispute and human insecurity. This makes it difficult for the private and industrial sectors to operate effectively and expand their investments on the continent. Policies, regulations and institutional frameworks could be put in place to ensure that biofuel production for instance does not degrade the environment, create land disputes and compromise food production. A good model as practiced in India where Jatropha planted on wastelands were intercropped or mixed with food crops could be explored.

Ecosystem management needs to be given the utmost attention. (UNESCO, 2011). The hydrological circle is a biophysical process that depends on the ecosystem as a "service provider" for continuous flow, natural pollutant treatment, water purification and control of runoff. Therefore, there is the need for a massive development of capacities of community members in watershed management, without adversely affecting soil and water (Zamora and Ken, 2010). This can be done using agro-forestry system and other green technologies. This offers numerous benefits such as restoration of riparian and wetland ecosystems, improvement in water and soil quality and reduction in flooding, runoff and runoff transported sediments.

Lakes in Africa still remain a veritable source of fresh water. This notwithstanding, many are understudied and neglected, some heavily polluted while others are shrinking in size with a significant build-up of sediments making navigation, fishing and livelihood survival on them difficult. More research is still needed for the management of lakes in Africa in areas like water resource management, socioeconomic aspects, restoration, ecosystem degradation, pollution and exploitation. A sound regulatory framework for effective management of the water resources is still lacking in most Sub-Saharan Africa (SSA) countries. Only about 3% of Africa's renewable water resources have been tapped, therefore

opportunities exist for tapping and harvesting more water for food,
irrigation, domestic and industrial use.

FAOSTAT (2009) and IFPRI (2010) put the total of Africa's cultivated
land under irrigation at 6 % compared to 37 % in Asia and 14 % in Latin
America. This indicates that a great opportunity exists for bringing more
hectares under irrigation. The arid and semi-arid ecologies receive some
rainfall annually; therefore, potentials exist in infield water management.
Agricultural intensification to feed the population (food security) impacts
severely on land and water resources. As it leaves the land degraded, the
heavy agro-chemicals and other inputs (liquid and solid) are washed by
runoff into water bodies. The enrichment of water bodies with applied
plant nutrients and other agro-chemical (pollutants) by runoff increases
aquatic weed infestation that poses a problem to navigation, creates
wastewater, water scarcity, non-availability of water and poverty.

New research will need to incorporate agriculture as the solution rather
than treating it as a causative agent of the problem as is currently being
done. Sustainable agricultural intensification should be the slogan in the
journey to food security in the continent. For the slogan to be translated
into action with tangible results, the capacity of smallholder farmers
must be developed in the area of improved agricultural practices to
minimise environmental impacts. This area will include integrated plant
nutrient management, integrated pest management, conservation
agriculture and livestock waste management (Mateo-sagasta and Burke,
2008).

In addition, capacities in rainwater and runoff harvesting, low input
technologies that improve water-use efficiencies (WUE) on the farm,
have to be undertaken and implemented in the field by the smallholder
farmer. Although wastewater is unpleasant and common, it can be
treated and reuse   for agriculture purposes. This should be prioritised in
research since most crops, leafy and green vegetables produced in urban
areas rely mainly on wastewater irrigation.

References

FAOSTAT 2009. FAO AQUASTAT: http://www.fao.org/nr/water/aquastat/dbase/index.stm>. (Retrieved May 10, 2012).

Garg, K. K.; Karlberg, L.; Wani, S. P.; Berndes, Göran 2011. Jatropha production on wastelands in India: opportunities and trade-offs for soil and water management at the watershed scale, Biofuel, Bioproducts & Biorefining. 5 (4) s 410 -430.

IFPRI. 2010. What is irrigation potentials for Africa? A biophysical and socioeconomic approach. IFPRI discussion paper 00993. Pp40

Lal, R. 2008 Preface. In: Junge B, Abiadoo, R, Chikoye, D & Stahr, B. (eds) Soil and water conservation in Nigeria past and present on-station and on-farm initiative. Soil and Water Conservation Society, Ankeny, Lowa, USA. 48pp.

Mateo-sagasta, J and Burke, J. 2008. Agriculture and water quality interaction; a global overview. SOLAW background thematic report – TRO8, pp 46

UNESCO 2011. Facts and figures: managing water under uncertainty and risk. United Nations World Water development Report 4. P16.

United Nations International Development Organisation (UNIDO), 2009. Scaling up renewable energy in Africa. UNIDO, Vienna. Pp32.

United Nations University Institute for Natural Resources in Africa (UNU-INRA). 2011. *Strategic plan 2011 – 2014.*

Zamora, Diomy and Ken, B. 2010. Agroforestry: role in watershed management. http://ssc.bibalex.org/viewer/detail.jsf;jsessionid. Retrieved January 23, 2012

Printed in the United States
By Bookmasters